KEY STAGE 3

MATHEMATICS

Brian Speed

LONGMAN

HOMEWORK HANDBOOKS

Series editors:

Geoff Black and Stuart Wall

Other titles in this series:

ENGLISH
FRENCH
GERMAN
SCIENCE

Addison Wesley Longman Ltd.
Edinburgh Gate, Harlow
Essex CM20 2JE
England
and Associated Companies throughout the world.

© Addison Wesley Longman Ltd. 1996

First Published 1996

ISBN 0582 29328-6

British Library Cataloguing in Publication Data
A catalogue record for this title is available from the British Library

Set in Stone by 30

Printed in Great Britain by Henry Ling Ltd., at the Dorset Press, Dorchester, Dorset

INTRODUCTION

This book will help you with all the mathematics you will encounter in your Key Stage 3 mathematics lessons.

You will find in this book entries, arranged in alphabetical order, on a variety of terms and topics relevant to Key Stage 3 mathematics. In some cases (the entry on *equations* for example) the entries are quite detailed. In other cases where only a brief definition is needed the entries are quite short.

Where reference is made to another entry in the book, bold italic lettering is used as in the following example:

AXIS

An axis is the straight line that you use to put your scales on a *graph*. The common ones are the x-axis (horizontal) and the y-axis (vertical).

⟐ *gradient* and Figure G.6

This means that the book also contains an entry on graphs and that you might find it helpful to refer to these when thinking about axis. At the bottom of some entries you will come across the symbol ⟐ . Entries next to this symbol can also be turned to for extra help (here, turn to gradient when thinking about axis).

There are plenty of examples to help you understand how to work through questions and how to answer them. There are also a lot of example Key Stage 3 test questions, with a full solution showing how to answer the question and to warn you about some of the common errors.

The book is not written to be read from cover to cover, but to dive into to give you more information and help on any point or topic which you find difficult or for which you may just want another explanation.

This book will help you as you work on your homework. It will not do the homework for you, but it will certainly give you extra help and practice in tackling any problem you face.

To the student

This book is written so that you can read it, not from front to back, but as you need it. Keep it handy, so that when you have your mathematics homework then you can look up the topic and remind yourself of what it was that you did in school.

If you have been away from school for any reason then you can use this book to help teach you the missing topic so that you do not get behind in your work.

Before your year examinations, or any short mid-term tests, then you can use the book to revise the topics you have covered in class. You should also practise the example Key Stage 3 questions which appear throughout the book (try not to look at the solution under the question until you have attempted to answer the question yourself).

To the parent

Although this book is written to be read by your son/daughter it can also remind you of the topics which you have long forgotten. You may find that your son/daughter is learning some new topics in the book or he/she may have been taught an approach which is very different from 'how we did it when we went to school!' This book covers these new topics and shows the approaches used in schools today, and this will help *you* to help your son/daughter.

You will see example Key Stage 3 questions which will give you an idea of the way questions may be asked on a particular topic.

But do beware!! The book covers *all* the Key Stage 3 work and you may find some work that your child has not yet met or will not meet, so do not think you have to know *everything* in the book (*not* just yet anyhow).

ACKNOWLEDGEMENTS

I am indebted to my own children James, John, Joseph and Joy who I have constantly kept in mind while writing this book. To my wife Gillian, who stopped asking for the jobs to be done for a while, and to Stuart Wall and Geoff Black, the editing team who gave quiet encouragement at all stages of production.

I am also grateful to all those people who allowed me to go to so many Key Stage 3 meetings to discuss the national papers and how they will be marked. And of course I am grateful to the many students whose papers I have marked for showing me so many different, ingenious ways of answering questions. (Not always right, but often quite ingenious!)

ACUTE ANGLE

This is the description of an angle that has a size smaller than a right angle; in other words, an acute angle is less than 90°.

 angles

ADJACENT

This is a special name given to one of the sides of a right angled triangle when we are involved in some *trigonometry* (Figure A.1).

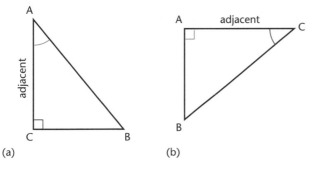

(a) (b)

Figure A.1

Adjacent means 'next to'. In the case of a right angled triangle we are often concerned with finding the adjacent side. This is often easiest to find by eliminating two of the three sides:

● Eliminate the *hypotenuse* – the side opposite the right angle.

● Eliminate the side opposite the angle in question.

● The remaining side is the adjacent side.

In Figure A.1a the angle being considered is $\widehat{CAB}$. The side adjacent to $\widehat{CAB}$ is therefore AC. In Figure A.1b the angle being considered is $\widehat{ACB}$. The side adjacent to $\widehat{ACB}$ is therefore AC. Notice how the adjacent side is the one next to both the right angle and the angle being considered.

ALGEBRA

This is the use of letters for numbers and is often known as the language of mathematics. The basic language of algebra is shown by the following examples:

$5 + x$	meaning 5 added to x
$t - 4$	meaning take 4 away from t
$3y$	meaning 3 multiplied by y (note we do not use the multiplication sign)
$\dfrac{x}{5}$	means x divided by 5
x^2	means the square of x, that is x, multiplied by itself

There are a lot of different questions that can be solved using algebra.

Simplification

Only *like* terms can be added or subtracted, as follows:

$$3x + 4x = 7x \quad 6x - 2x = 4x \quad 3x^2 + 4x^2 = 7x^2$$
$$5y + y = 6y \quad 4t - t = 3t \quad 3y^3 + 2y^3 = 6y^3$$

Substitution

This is where you replace a letter with a number. For example, the value of $3t + 2$ when $t = 4$ is found by replacing t with 4, giving

$$3 \times 4 + 2 = 12 + 2 = 14$$

Example KS3 question

Four people each have a card:

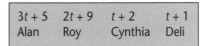

$3t + 5$	$2t + 9$	$t + 2$	$t + 1$
Alan	Roy	Cynthia	Deli

(a) Work out the value for t which will make Alan's and Roy's cards worth the same as each other.

(b) There are two people whose cards will never be worth the same as each other. Who are they? Explain your answer.

Solution

(a) We need to write down the cards equal to each other as

$$3t + 5 = 2t + 9$$

This gives us an equation that we need to solve. Move the $2t$ and the 5 to the other side of the equation and make them do the opposite thing. Hence

$$3t - 2t = 9 - 5$$
$$t = 4$$

(b) Cynthia's and Deli's cards can never be the same since when you put their cards together, you get $t + 2 = t + 1$. This could only happen if $2 = 1$, which it can't!

All the other cards can be put together to form an equation that you could solve.

✦ *equations, factor, formula, generalise, simplification, substitution*

ALTERNATE ANGLES

✦ *transversal*

AND RULE

✦ *independent, probability*

ANGLES

An angle is made when two straight lines come together. There are four types of angle:

(a) Right angle   (b) Acute angle

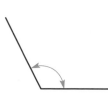

(c) Obtuse angle   (d) Reflex angle

Figure A.2 Different angles

- The *right angle* (Figure A.2a) you *must* know so as to recognise the others.

- The *acute angle* (Figure A.2b) is smaller than a right angle.

- The *obtuse angle* (Figure A.2c) is bigger than a right angle, but less than two right angles.

- The *reflex angle* (Figure A.2d) is bigger than two right angles next to each other.

You measure the size of an angle with a **protractor**.

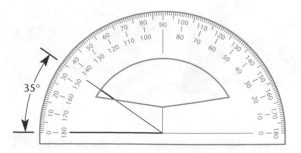

(a)

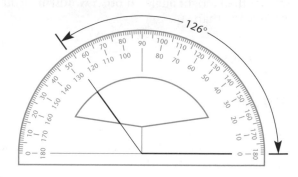

(b)

Figure A.3 Using a protractor

- Notice how we have used the protractor in Figure A.3a to measure an angle of 35°.

- Notice how we measure an angle of 126° in Figure A.3b.

You do need to be confident in the use of a protractor; only *practice* will help.
  Use your protractor to measure the angles in Figure A.4.

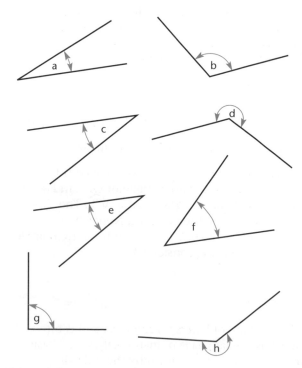

Figure A.4

Now just draw any ten angles yourself and practise measuring them until you can use your protractor with confidence.

✦ *polygon, supplementary angles, trigonometry, vertically opposite angles*

APPROXIMATION

We all use approximations every day: 'There are about 30 in our class', or 'It takes about twenty minutes to get home.'

We approximate by *rounding* off information, either as a comparison or as a calculation.

Comparison

We can show the idea of comparison by looking at the picture in Figure A.5.

Figure A.5

It shows a man standing next to a tree. How tall is the tree?

If we assume the man to be of average height, i.e. about 6 feet (180 cm), then the tree, which is about four times as big, will be 4 × 6 feet, which is 24 feet tall (4 × 180 cm = 7.2 metres).

Calculation

We calculate by rounding our numbers off to something easy to calculate with. So for example

$$\frac{3.45 \times 19.7}{5.42} \text{ will become } \frac{3 \times 20}{5}$$

We can divide the 5 into the 20 to get 4, so that the solution now becomes 3 × 4 which is 12. So our approximate answer will be 12.

✦ *rounding*

ARC

An arc is part of the *circumference* of a circle. Every arc has a *radius* (Figure A.6).

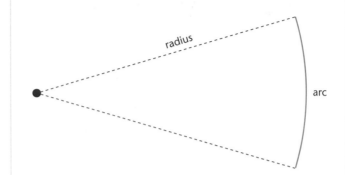

Figure A.6

If you know some information about the arc, such as its radius and the angle it makes at the centre of a circle, then you can find the length of the arc with this formula:

$$\text{arc length} = \frac{\text{angle} \times \pi \times 2 \times \text{radius}}{360}$$

where π (*pi*) is best keyed directly on your calculator, or may be taken as 3.142.

AREA

Area is the amount of space inside a flat shape.

You should know how to find the area of the following shapes.

Rectangle

In Figure A.7a,

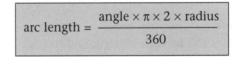

area = length × breadth

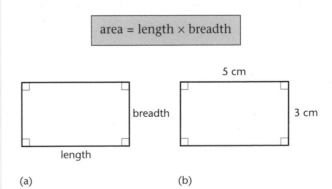

(a)   (b)

Figure A.7

Example 1

The area of the rectangle in Figure A.7b is 3 cm × 5 cm. This gives an area of 15 cm². Notice we use cm² as the units.

Triangle

In Figure A.8a,

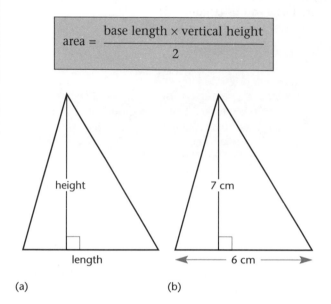

$$\text{area} = \frac{\text{base length} \times \text{vertical height}}{2}$$

(a)   (b)

Figure A.8

Example 2

The area of the *triangle* in Figure A.8b is half of 6 cm × 7 cm. This is half of 42 cm², that is 21 cm². Notice again the use of cm² as units.

Parallelogram

In Figure A.9a,

$$\text{area} = \text{base} \times \text{vertical height}$$

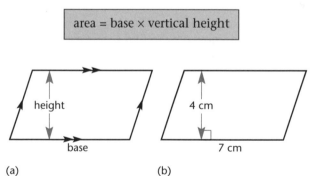

(a)   (b)

Figure A.9

Example 3

The area of the *parallelogram* in Figure A.9b is 7 cm × 4 cm. This gives an area of 28 cm².

Circle

In Figure A.10a,

$$\text{area} = \pi \times (\text{radius})^2$$

If you are given the diameter, halve this to get the radius.

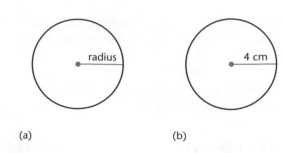

(a)   (b)

Figure A.10

Example 4

The area of the *circle* in Figure A.10b is given by $\pi \times 4^2$. This gives an area of $\pi \times 16 = 50.3$ cm².

Note that we should use a calculator to solve this problem and key the calculator value of π. The answer will then need rounding off.

If you do not have a calculator with a π key then use the value of 3.142 as a reasonable approximation, but you still need to round off your answer to about three figures.

Example KS3 question

Work out the area of the shapes in Figure A.11.

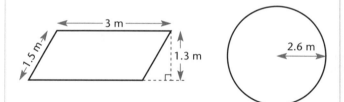

(a) Parallelogram   (b) Circle

Figure A.11

Solution

(a) The area of a parallelogram is the vertical height × the base length. In Figure A.11a the area, is 1.3 m × 3 m, which is 3.9 m². (The common error here is to try to use all the lengths given; but as you can see, we do *not* need to use the slant height of 1.5 m.)

(b) The area of a circle is given by $\pi \times (\text{radius})^2$. In Figure A.11b the area is $\pi \times 2.6^2 = \pi \times 6.76$, which is 21.2 m². (The common error here is to multiply π by 2.6, then to square that result.)

ARITHMETIC MEAN

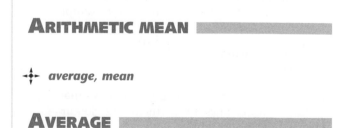

✦ *average, mean*

AVERAGE

There are three different types of average that you need to be familiar with:

1 The *mean*: this is found by adding together all the items in a list and dividing by the number of items in that list. It is the average that is most commonly used.

2 The *median*: this is the item that appears in the middle of your list once you have arranged your list in numerical order.

3 The *mode*: this is the item in a list that appears more times than any other item.

Example
From the list 1, 1, 2, 3, 3, 6, 6, 8, 8, 8, 9:

- The mean is 5, since the numbers add up to 55 and there are 11 of them, so the mean is $55 \div 11$ which is 5.

- The median is 6, since it is in the middle of the numbers in order.

- The mode is 8, since no other number appears as many times.

Example KS3 question
Steve has five dogs. Their ages are 2 years, 2 years, 3 years, 4 years, 9 years.

- The mean age of the dogs is 4.

- The median age of the dogs is 3.

- The mode age of the dogs is 2.

Ritu also has five dogs. The mean, median and mode ages of her dogs are the same as those of Steve's dogs. But not all of Ritu's dogs have the same ages as Steve's dogs! What ages could they be?

Solution
The simplest way to answer this is just to change the ages of two dogs, making one a year older and the other a year younger. By doing this the mean stays the same.

But we need to keep the median at 3 and the mode at 2. So, we change the ages of the 4-year-old and the 9-year-old, adding 1 to the 4 to make 5, and taking 1 off the 9 to make 8. So, Ritu's dogs could be 2, 2, 3, 5, 8 years old.

✤ *frequency, mean, median, mode*

AXIS

An axis is the straight line that you use to put your scales on a *graph*. The common ones are the *x*-axis (horizontal) and the *y*-axis (vertical).

✤ *gradient* and Figure G.6

AXIS OF SYMMETRY

✤ *symmetry*

Bar chart

A bar chart is a display of information. The bars can be any thickness but they will have gaps between them. The bars can be either vertical or horizontal. Look at the two examples in Figure B.1.

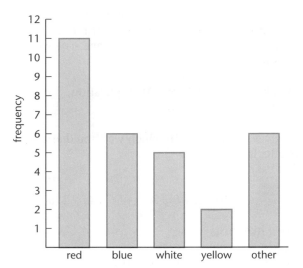

(a) Vertical bar chart

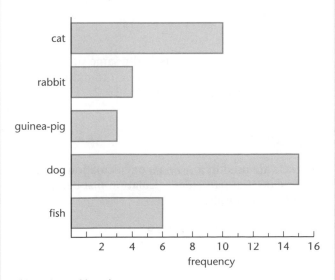

(b) Horizontal bar chart

Figure B.1

The vertical bar chart in Figure B.1a shows how many cars going past a school in one hour had different colours. The horizontal bar chart in Figure B.1b shows the favourite pets of year 9 in a school.

Note that the word *frequency* means the number of times that something occurs.

Bearing

Bearings are presented to help you find directions. There are different types of bearings as follows.

Compass bearings

The compass in Figure B.2a shows all the bearings that you need to be familiar with. Notice the pattern that helps you to fix points such as NE and SW which fall *between* the main bearings.

Three figure bearings

The compass in Figure B.2b is just like the one in Figure B.2a, but also has the three figure bearings on it. These represent the angles measured clockwise from north. The important bearings to remember are the following:

north (000°), east (090°), south (180°), west (270°)

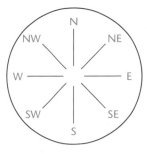 

(a) Compass bearings   (b) Three figure bearings

Figure B.2

There are other ways to give bearings but none of them should be used instead of the methods shown above. Always give bearings using compass or three figure methods.

Example

From Figure B.3 we can say the following:

Using eight point *compass* bearings:

- Emily is due east of Helen.
- Douglas is due south of Emily.
- Joseph is north-west of Douglas.
- Helen is north of Joseph.
- Emily is north-east of Joseph, etc.

Using *three figure* bearings:

- Emily is on a bearing of 090° from Helen.
- Emily is on a bearing of 045° from Joseph.
- Douglas is on a bearing of 135° from Joseph.
- Douglas is on a bearing of 140° from Helen, etc.

Helen

Emily

Joseph

Douglas

Figure B.3

Example KS3 question

A plane flies on a bearing of 250° from the airport. Draw a sketch to illustrate the airport and the bearing of 250°.

Solution

You need to remember that a bearing of west is 270°, so 250° is just a little bit down (south) from west.

The question requires a sketch, so we do not need to get the protractor out (but you could if you wished). You should indicate where north is and which angle is 250°. Your diagram then should look rather like Figure B.4.

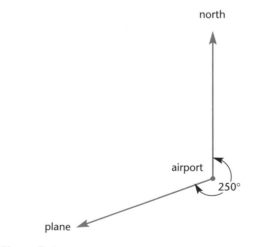

Figure B.4

BILLION

A billion is a thousand million, that is 10^9 or 1 000 000 000.

BINARY DIGIT

✛ *bit*

BIT

All data stored in computer memory is represented using binary logic. Each binary digit, or bit, can be set to a 1 or a 0.

BODMAS

BODMAS is a word to help you remember the order in which you should work out an arithmetical problem involving more than one stage. The word stands for:

Brackets, **O**f, **D**ivision, **M**ultiplication, **A**ddition, **S**ubtraction

This gives us the order in which we should arrange our calculations.

For example,

$$10 \div 2 + 8 \times 3 - \tfrac{1}{2} \text{ of } 6 + (4 - 2)$$

is done like this:

Brackets	$10 \div 2 + 8 \times 3 - \tfrac{1}{2} \text{ of } 6 + 2$	
Of	$10 \div 2 + 8 \times 3 - 3$	$+ 2$
Division	$5 + 8 \times 3 - 3$	$+ 2$
Multiplication	$5 + 24 - 3$	$+ 2$ (note $5 + 24$
Addition	$31 - 3$	$+ 2 = 31$)
Subtraction	28	

If any two or more numbers of the same sign are next to each other we work from left to right. For example, $10 - 6 - 2$ will be $4 - 2 = 2$.

BRACKETS

Brackets are used in a *formula* or calculation to make sure we do that particular calculation *first* before all others. For example,

$$6 + (5 - 2) = 6 + 3 = 9$$
$$(4 - 1) \times (12 - 5) = 3 \times 7 = 21$$

BYTE

This is the number of *bits* used to represent one character. One byte is usually taken as representing 8 bits.

✛ *bit*

CALCULATORS

You can use your calculator in the Key Stage 3 exams but there will be some questions where you cannot use it. If there is such a question it will clearly tell you *not* to use your calculator in this question.

You really ought to have your own calculator with all the functions on it, and you should get plenty of practice in using it at school. Your teacher should advise you on which type of calculator is the best for you. If you are in any doubt then most people require a simple *scientific calculator* for most of their school days.

You need to be familiar with your own calculator so that you know how to perform all the tasks you need on it. When using a calculator in any test, though, still remember to *show* all your working out, such as which numbers you multiplied together.

Get used to using the *memory* in your calculator so that you do not work with rounded-off answers in the middle of calculations. You should leave any *rounding* to the end of the question.

Example KS3 question

You have to find the answer to this calculation:

$$\frac{70^2 - 28^2}{8 \times 17}$$

Show which keys you press on the calculator.

Solution

There is more than one correct solution to this problem. What is being tested is whether you can you use your calculator efficiently.

● Method 1: press the keys in Figure C.1.

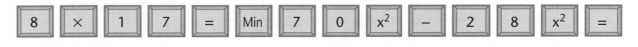

Figure C.1

● Method 2: press the keys in Figure C.2.

Figure C.2

You will see that method 2 is shorter than method 1 but it involves knowing how to divide by a product (multiplication) quickly.

There are other quite valid methods; try these and any others you are familiar with and check that you get the answer 30.264 706.

This answer could then be rounded, say to three decimal places, giving an answer of 30.265.

CANCELLING

This is what we call an attempt to make *fractions* into easier numbers to handle. We divide the top and the bottom by any number that will go exactly into both of them. The biggest number that will go exactly into both top (*numerator*) and bottom (*denominator*) is the best for cancelling.

For example,

$$\frac{9}{15} = \frac{3}{5} \quad \text{by dividing both top and bottom by 3}$$

and

$$\frac{48}{84} = \frac{4}{7} \quad \text{by dividing both top and bottom by 12}$$

CAPACITY

Capacity is the amount of a liquid or a gas that can be held in a container.

The common units for capacity are litres or cubic centimetres (cm^3). A *litre* is equal to 1000 cm^3. Hence a container with a volume of 1000 cm^3 will have a capacity of 1 litre.

A millilitre is one-thousandth of a litre and is approximately equal to 1 cm^3.

 *milli*

CENTIMETRE

A hundredth of a metre: 100 centimetres equal 1 metre.

The unit symbol for centimetre is cm.

2.54 centimetres are approximately equivalent to 1 inch.

CENTRE

Centre of enlargement

This is the point from which the lines are drawn in order to enlarge a shape. Figure C.3a shows an *enlargement* of the triangle ABC with a *scale* factor 3 from the centre of enlargement *. The enlargement is triangle PQR.

Centre of rotation

This is the point around which a shape will rotate. Figure C.3b shows a *rotation* through 90° clockwise around *, the centre of rotation. The triangle ABC has rotated to triangle A'B'C'.

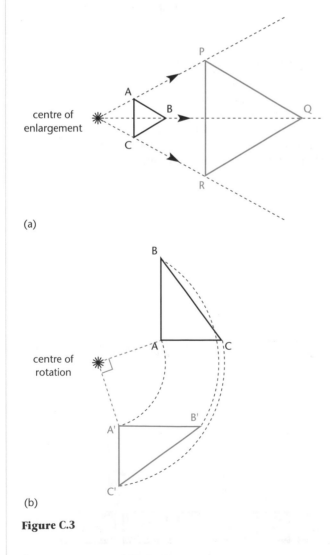

(a)

(b)

Figure C.3

⟵⟶ *enlargement, rotation*

CENTURY

A hundred. 'Century' is the common word for 100 years in age or 100 runs in a game of cricket.

CHANGE OF SUBJECT

We move a *formula* around in order to change the *subject* of the formula.

For example, in the formula $t = 3p + m$ the variable t is the subject of the formula since we have the letter t on its own to the left of the equals sign. To change the subject to, say, p we have to move all the numbers and letters so that p alone is on one side of the equals sign. We first move the thing that is furthest away from the p, and when we have moved it onto the other side of the equals sign we make it do the opposite thing. Hence, from

$$t = 3p + m$$

move the m to give

$$t - m = 3p \quad \text{(the sign then changes)}$$

move the 3 to give

$$\frac{t - m}{3} = p \quad \text{(divide both sides by 3)}$$

and now turn it all round to give

$$p = \frac{t - m}{3} \quad \text{(to get } p \text{ on the left hand side)}$$

CIRCLE

A circle is the set of points which are a particular distance away from a given point, called the centre of the circle.

You need to know the words that go with a circle, as we can see in Figure C.4.

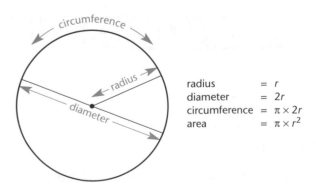

radius	$= r$
diameter	$= 2r$
circumference	$= \pi \times 2r$
area	$= \pi \times r^2$

Figure C.4

● The outside edge of the circle is called the *circumference*.

- Any straight line from the centre of the circle to the circumference is called a *radius*.

- Any straight line going through the centre of the circle from circumference to circumference is known as a *diameter*.

> Remember: that diameter = 2 × radius.

- The length of the circumference of a circle is called the *perimeter* of the circle and is given by the rule

circumference = π × diameter

where π is approximately 3.142 or more accurately is found on your calculator with the π key.

- The area of the circle is given by the rule

area = π × (radius)²

In problems you need to check whether the radius or the diameter has been given, and then correctly use what has been given in your solution.

Example 1

Find the circumference and the area of a circle of radius 6 cm.

circumference = π × (2 × 6) = 37.7 cm (rounded to one decimal place)

area = π × 6² = π × 36 = 113 cm²
(rounded to the nearest whole number)

Example 2

Find the circumference and the area of a circle of diameter 6 cm.

circumference = π × 6 = 18.8 cm (rounded to one decimal place)

area = π × (6 ÷ 2)² = π × 3² = π × 9 = 28.3 cm² (rounded to one decimal place)

Example KS3 question

The perimeter of the shaded shape in Figure C.5a is made using the stages shown in Figure C.5b, namely one large semicircular arc and three equal small semicircular arcs. Calculate (a) the perimeter and (b) the area of the shaded shape.

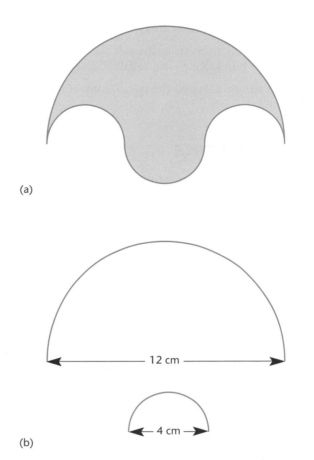

(a)

(b)

Figure C.5

Solution

(a) We need to find half the circumference of the large circle, and three half circumferences of the small circle. Here we can use the formula

circumference = π × diameter

- Half the large circle circumference will be half of π × 12 = 18.849 556 (put this into calculator memory, you may need it).

- Half the small circle circumference will be half of π × 4 = 6.283 185 3. So three of these half small circle circumferences will be this multiplied by 3, which is 18.849 556.

- Hence the total perimeter is your display multiplied by 2, which when rounded off gives 37.7 cm.

 (OK, we didn't need that number in the calculator memory, but we didn't know that at the time, did we?!!)

(b) We now do a similar thing for the area. Find half the area of the large circle, and half the area of the small circle. (Note: the shaded shape is *minus* two *plus* one half of the area of the small circle. In other words we subtract one half area of the small circle.) Here we can use the formula

area = π × (radius)²

- Half the large circle area = ½ × π × 6² = 56.548 668 (put this into the calculator memory).

- Half the small circle's area $= \frac{1}{2} \times \pi \times 2^2 = 6.283\ 185$.
- Now subtract this from the calculator memory and we get 50.3 cm² (rounded).

  (You see we *did* need the calculator memory this time!)

CIRCUMFERENCE

The circumference is the outside edge of a **circle**. Its length can be calculated by the formula

> circumference = π × diameter

where π is the value 3.142 or is more accurately found as a key on your calculator.

Example KS3 question

Hussain runs along the path sketched in Figure C.6. The curved part of the path is a semicircle. How far does he run if he goes once round the path?

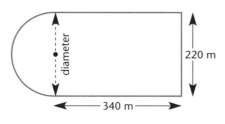

Figure C.6

Solution

We are looking for the **perimeter** of this shape, which is three straight bits and half a circumference.

- The half circumference part will be found by $\frac{1}{2} \times \pi \times$ diameter. So this will be

  $\frac{1}{2} \times \pi \times 220 = 345.6$ m (rounded).

- Add this to the straight bits and you get

  $340 + 340 + 220 + 345.6 = 1245.6$ m $= 1.246$ km

COEFFICIENTS

A coefficient is the number in front of a letter in an *algebra* expression. For example:

- In $3x$ the coefficient of x is 3.
- In $5x^2$ the coefficient of x^2 is 5.

COMBINATIONS

Combinations of items involve the collection of different pairs (or groups) of those items. We must decide whether the *order* of the items makes any difference or not.

Example 1

I toss two coins. What different combinations of coins can I have?

Think of tossing two different coins, coin A and coin B. The different combinations of heads and tails can be put into a list as follows:

Coin A	Coin B
head	head
head	tail
tail	head
tail	tail

If we decide that the order does matter, then we have four different combinations. You can see that the combination of a head and a tail can happen twice as many times as that of two heads or two tails.

> *If we had decided that the order did not matter we might have seen a head and a tail as being the same as a tail and a head, and so ended up with three possible combinations.*

Example 2

In my top drawer I have three jumpers, one red, one blue, one black. In my bottom drawer I have three hats, one blue, one yellow, one green. What are the different combinations of colour I can wear when I have a jumper and a hat?

Put the combinations into a list with some order.

Jumper	Hat	Jumper	Hat	Jumper	Hat
red	blue	blue	blue	black	blue
red	yellow	blue	yellow	black	yellow
red	green	blue	green	black	green

You can now see that there are nine different combinations you can make.

Example KS3 question

Two spinners are shown in Figure C.7.

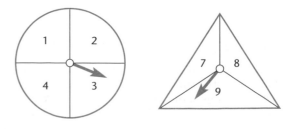

Figure C.7

If you spun the arrow on both of the spinners, you could get the number 3 followed by the number 9. This can be written as (3, 9).

Write down all of the combinations of numbers you could get using both spinners, including (3, 9).

Solution

Write down the possible combinations in a list, smallest number first, so that you do not miss any possible combination.

(1, 7) (2, 7) (3, 7) (4, 7)
(1, 8) (2, 8) (3, 8) (4, 8)
(1, 9) (2, 9) (3, 9) (4, 9)

So there are 12 different combinations.

COMMON FACTOR

Common factors are the *factors* that two (or more) numbers have in common. A factor is a number that divides *exactly* into another number.

For example, the common factors of 24 and 18 are 1, 2, 3 and 6, since all these numbers divide exactly into both 24 and 18. The *highest common factor* (HCF) here is 6.

COMMON MULTIPLES

Common multiples are the multiples that two (or more) numbers have in common.

For example, some common multiples of 6 and 9 are 18, 36, 54 and so on, since both 6 and 9 divide exactly into all these numbers. The *lowest common multiple* (LCM) here is 18.

COMPASS

A compass is an instrument for showing *bearings*. Figure B.2a on page 7 is often called the eight point compass.

COMPASSES

A pair of compasses is a piece of geometrical equipment used for drawing *circles* (Figure C.8).

Figure C.8 Pair of compasses

You do need to be able to use compasses to draw any size of circle asked. Again it is only practice that will make you better at using compasses.

COMPLEMENTARY

Angles are complementary if they add up to 90°.

COMPOUND INTEREST

This is when interest is built up on top of previous interest.

For example, suppose you have £10 in a bank that pays you 8% interest each year. At the end of year 1 it pays you £0.80 interest, so that you now have £10.80 in the account. At the end of year 2 it will pay you 8% of £10.80 as interest, which is £0.86. This when added to your account gives you £11.66 altogether at the end of year 2.

This process of receiving compound interest continues as long as the money is in the bank each year. You can see that the interest also earns interest as it builds up, year on year.

simple interest

CONE

A cone is a three dimensional shape, as shown in Figure C.9. Its base is a circle of *radius r*, and the *vertex* (top point) is usually directly above the centre of the circle.

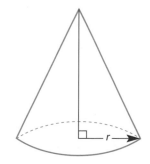

Figure C.9

pyramid

CONGRUENT

Two shapes are congruent if they are exactly the same. In other words if you put one shape exactly on top of the other and they completely match up, then the shapes are congruent.

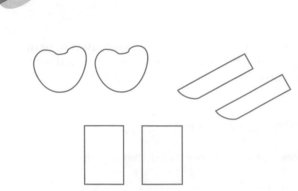

Figure C.10

Figure C.10 presents some pairs of congruent shapes.

CONSTRUCT

To construct is to draw something with ruler and *compasses*, only using a protractor if you are asked to.
  Here are some constructions you should be familiar with.

A right angle

To construct a *right angle* at the point D on the line AB in Figure C.11 use a pair of compasses with an arc of about 3 cm. Then with the sharp end of the compasses on point D, draw two little arcs either side of point D on the line as shown. Now make the arc of your compasses bigger, say at about 5 cm. Put the sharp end of the compasses on each little arc in turn (where the arcs cut the line AB), and draw a bigger arc above point D. You should now have two bigger arcs that cross over each other directly above point D as in the diagram. Now join point D to where these arcs cross and you will have created a right angle at D.

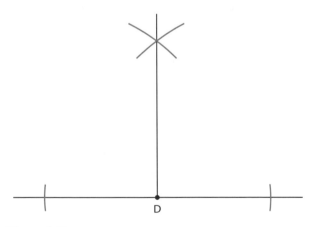

Figure C.11

A 60° angle

To construct a 60° angle at point A on the line AB shown in Figure C.12, set your pair of compasses at about 4 cm. Now put the sharp end at point A and draw an arc (here a quarter circle) from above point A to the line AB. Then keeping the compasses at the *same* distance, put the sharp end of the compasses to where the first arc cut the line AB, and draw another

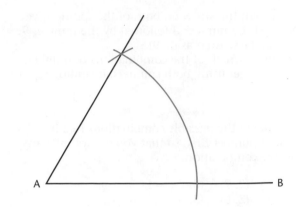

Figure C.12

little arc which just cuts the first arc made. Now join the point A to where your two arcs cross and you have an angle of 60°.

Construction errors

The most common errors in constructions are:

1 To be not accurate enough. Your measurements should be correct within 1 mm and your angles also should be correct within 1 degree. If you have been asked to construct there is nothing wrong with using your ruler and protractor to check what you have done; then if you are inaccurate you can redraw as necessary, provided you have the time.

2 To use equipment that does not allow you to construct, like set squares and protractors – or even to guess!

Always show all the construction lines so that an examiner can tell that you have constructed. If there are no visible lines of construction, then the examiner will assume that you have used other means and give you no marks at all.

CONTINUOUS

Data is called continuous if it can take any value. Continuous data therefore needs *rounding* off to some degree of accuracy. The types of data that are continuous include length, weight, time and capacity. A continuous scale is one you will use for most graphs, giving you the opportunity to put any values on the axes of your graph within the given range and to a certain level of accuracy.

CONVERSION GRAPHS

 graphs

CO-ORDINATES

A co-ordinate is a pair of numbers that pin-points an exact position on a *graph*.

It is a pair of numbers written something like (2, 5). The 2 refers to the point being 2 units horizontally out from the origin, and the 5 refers to the point being 5 units up from the origin. This is important since the biggest mistake students make is to get these two the wrong way round.

Look at Figure C.13 and notice that each point is a certain number of units *out* and a certain number *up* from the **origin**, which is (0, 0):

A (2, 1)   D (1, 5)   F (5, 0)
B (4, 2)   E (0, 3)   G (5½, 3½)
C (3, 3)

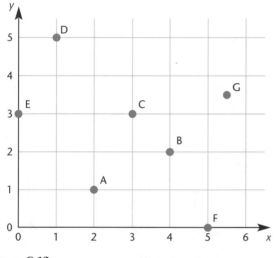

Figure C.13

CORRELATION

'Correlation' is the word usually used to indicate a relationship between two (or more) variables. A correlation is usually shown on a *scatter graph*.

A correlation exists between two things if there is a connection between them, for example:

● The taller you are, the bigger sized shoes you take.

● The hotter the temperature, the more ice cream is sold.

● The more expensive the seats, the fewer will be sold.

Correlation can be seen on the scatter diagram in Figure C.14a. A **line of best fit** can be drawn if there is a correlation, showing the *trend* of the data.

Positive correlation

This is where the trend is such that both items get bigger or smaller with each other (Figure C.14b).

Negative (or inverse) correlation

This is where the trend is such that one item gets bigger while the other item gets smaller (Figure C.14c).

 scatter graph

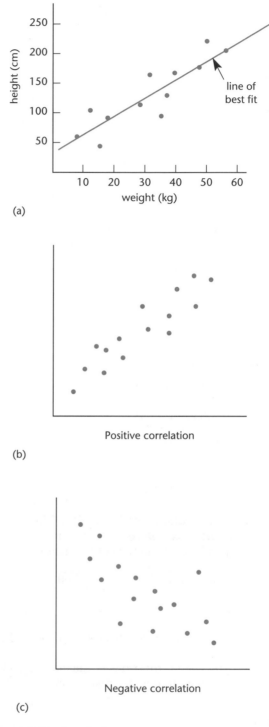

(a)

(b)

Positive correlation

(c)

Negative correlation

Figure C.14 Correlation

COSINE (cos)

Cosine (abbreviated cos) is used in *trigonometry* and is a ratio that will help you solve problems involving *right angled triangles*. The cosine of an angle in a right angled triangle is the side *adjacent* to the angle divided by the *hypotenuse* of the triangle. Look at Figure C.15a. The definition of cosine θ is

$$\cos \theta = \frac{\text{adjacent}}{\text{hypotenuse}}$$

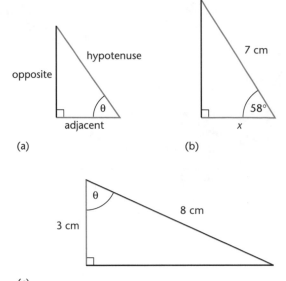

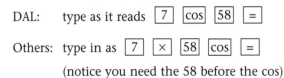

(c)

Figure C.15

Example 1

Find the length *x* in Figure C.15b.

From the triangle we can say that:

$$\cos 58° = \frac{\text{adjacent}}{\text{hypotenuse}} = \frac{x}{7}$$

Then

$$7 \cos 58° = x$$

(7 cos 58° means 7 multiplied by cos 58°.) This is done on a ***scientific calculator*** by one of two methods depending on the type of calculator:

DAL: type as it reads   7 cos 58 =

Others: type in as   7 × 58 cos =

(notice you need the 58 before the cos)

Check that you can do this on *your* calculator to get *x* = 3.7 cm (rounded to one decimal place).

Example 2

Find the angle θ in Figure C.15c.

From the triangle we can say that:

$$\cos θ = \frac{\text{adjacent}}{\text{hypotenuse}} = \frac{3}{8}$$

So

$$\cos θ = \frac{3}{8} = 0.375$$

We use this fact to find the size of angle θ. With 0.375 in the calculator, type into the calculator cos⁻¹ which is usually found by

shift cos   or   inv cos   or   2ndf cos

Check that you can do this on *your* calculator to get θ = 68° (rounded to the nearest degree).

CROSS-SECTION

The cross-section of a ***solid shape*** is the shape you get when you slice that shape in a particular direction.

A shape has a ***regular*** cross-section if it has the same cross-section running all the way down its length (or height). If this happens the shape will be a prism. Some examples of regular cross-sections are shown in Figure C.16.

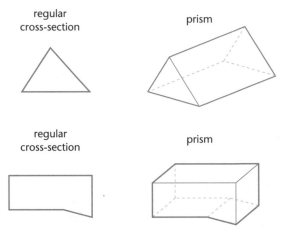

Figure C.16 Cross-section of various solid shapes

CUBE

A cube is a three dimensional ***solid shape*** with six square faces at right angles to each other (Figure C.17a).

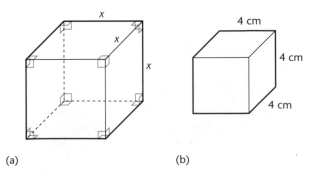

(a)   (b)

Figure C.17

A dice is in the shape of a cube.

The ***volume*** of a cube is found by multiplying its side length by itself twice.

volume of a cube = side length × side length
× side length
i.e. volume of a cube = (side length)³

For example, the volume of the cube with side length 4 cm shown in Figure C.17b is

$$4 \text{ cm} \times 4 \text{ cm} \times 4 \text{ cm} = 64 \text{ cm}^3$$

Notice the use of the units cm³.
   A net of a cube can be made in various ways.

+ *nets, solid shapes*

Cube of a number

To cube a number is to multiply it by itself twice. For example, the cube of 2 is $2 \times 2 \times 2$ which is 8. The cube numbers are 1^3, 2^3, 3^3, 4^3, 5^3, 6^3, etc., which work out to be 1, 8, 27, 64, 125, 216, etc.

CUBE ROOT

The cube root of a number is that number which when multiplied by itself twice gives that number. For example, the cube root of 1000 is 10 since $10 \times 10 \times 10$ is equal to 1000. In other words, $^3\sqrt{1000} = 10$. You may well find a cube root key on your calculator.

CUBOID

A cuboid is best described as having a 'shoe box' shape. It is a three dimensional *solid shape* in which each face is a *rectangle* and opposite faces are *congruent* (Figure C.18a).

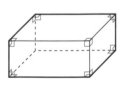
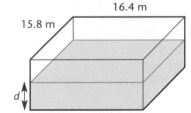

(a) Cuboid   (b) **Example KS3 question**

Figure C.18

Its *volume* is found by multiplying length by breadth by height.

volume of a cuboid = length × breadth × height

Example KS3 question

A pool is shown in Figure C.18b as being in the shape of a cuboid. It is 16.4 m long and 15.8 m wide. It is emptied for cleaning. 500 m³ of water are then poured into the pool. How deep is the water?

Solution

Let the height (i.e. depth) of water be d (I've put it on the diagram). The water in the pool will then take the shape of the pool, i.e. a cuboid. Then, from the equation for the volume of a cuboid,

volume of water = $16.4 \times 15.8 \times d = 259.12d$ m³

But the volume we are told is 500 m³. So

$$259.12d = 500$$

$$d = \frac{500}{259.12} = 1.93 \text{ m} \quad \text{(rounded)}$$

+ *nets, solid shapes*

CUMULATIVE FREQUENCY

This is what is commonly called a 'running total'.
   A cumulative frequency table is used to draw a cumulative frequency diagram, from which we can estimate the *median* as well as find *quartiles*.

Example

You will see that the following *frequency* table has had a cumulative frequency column placed alongside it, giving a running total. For example, a score of less than 10 marks has a frequency of 4, and a score between 11 and 20 marks has a frequency of 8; so the cumulative frequency (running total) for less than 20 marks is 12; and so on.

Score	Frequency	Cumulative frequency
1–10	4	4
11–20	8	12
21–30	12	24
31–40	36	60
41–50	16	76
51–60	9	85
61–70	5	90

The cumulative frequency column (running total) can now be plotted onto a cumulative frequency diagram, which could be either a curve or a polygon. Each of these has been drawn in Figure C.19 so that you can see the difference.

- The **cumulative frequency curve** uses a smooth curve to join the points (called the ogive).

- The **cumulative frequency polygon** uses straight lines to join the points.

Both types are used, and since the whole diagram is an approximation it will make little difference which you use, unless of course you are asked to *construct* one particular type in an exam. Then you should draw that particular type of cumulative frequency diagram.

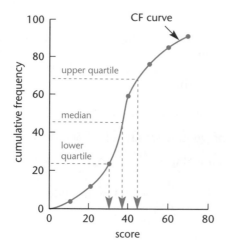

(a) Cumulative frequency (CF) curve

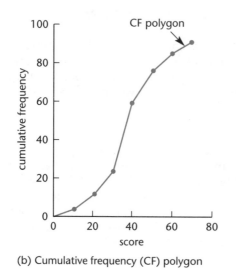

(b) Cumulative frequency (CF) polygon

Figure C.19

Notice how you can find the *median* by looking half-way along the cumulative frequency, and the *quartiles* (upper and lower) come at the quarter marks of the cumulative frequency.

Example KS3 question

Figure C.20 shows the cumulative frequency curve for women's wages.

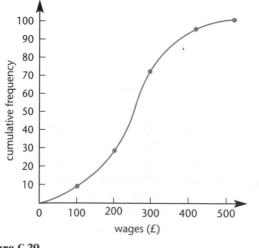

Figure C.20

(a) Complete the following table for men's wages, and put the men's cumulative frequency curve on the same graph as the women's.

Weekly wage (£)		Frequency	Cumulative frequency
at least	below		
0	100	2	
100	200	13	
200	300	39	
300	400	15	
400	500	31	

(b) Use the quartiles to compare the differences in the overall distribution of women's and men's wages.

Solution

(a) You must first complete the cumulative frequency column in the table and then draw the cumulative frequency curve.

(b) Next you need to find the upper and lower quartiles for each distribution from your curves. Then you can use these results to find the *inter-quartile range* for women and men as a means of comparing the differences in the overall distribution of their wages.

You should find statistics similar to the following:

	Women (£)	Men (£)
Lower quartile	195	240
Upper quartile	310	415
Inter-quartile range	115	175

You can now make suitable comments such as:

'The women's lower quartile is £45 below the men's, while the women's upper quartile is £105 below the men's.'

'The inter-quartile range for the women is only £115, compared with £175 for the men. This indicates that there is less spread or *dispersion* of pay around the average for women than for men. For example, most of the women are paid within £50 of the median women's pay of £260, while the men's pay is spread out far more with most men paid within £90 of their median wage of £295.'

'Clearly the pay of women is lagging behind the pay of men. The men have a larger proportion of high paid jobs than the women.'

✦ *frequency, inter-quartile range, quartiles*

CYCLIC QUADRILATERAL

✛ *quadrilateral*

CYLINDER

A cylinder is a three dimensional shape, rather like a cocoa tin or a drain pipe. Strictly speaking the cylinder is a *prism* with a regular *cross-section* in the shape of a *circle*, as shown in Figure C.21.

The *volume* of a cylinder is found by multiplying its end area by its length or height.

> volume of a cylinder = π × radius² × height

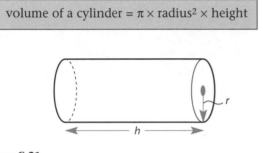

Figure C.21

In Figure C.21 the volume is $\pi r^2 h$.

Example

Find the volume of a cocoa tin of radius 3 cm and height 12 cm, as shown in Figure C.22a.

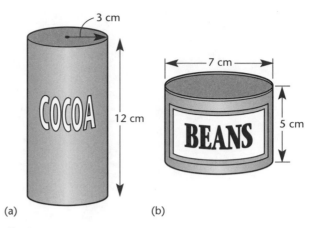

(a)   (b)

Figure C.22

$$
\begin{aligned}
\text{volume} &= \pi \times 3^2 \times 12 \\
&= \pi \times 9 \times 12 \\
&= 339 \text{ cm}^3 \text{ (rounded)}
\end{aligned}
$$

Example KS3 question

A tin of beans has the measurements shown in Figure C.22b. Work out the volume of the tin of beans.

Solution

We know that we need to use the formula: volume = $\pi r^2 h$. Since we are given the diameter, our first job is to halve this to get the radius of 3.5 cm. We can now substitute into the formula to get

$$
\text{volume} = \pi \times 3.5^2 \times 5 = 192 \text{ cm}^3 \text{ (rounded to nearest whole number)}
$$

DATA

Data is information available for use.
There are different types of data.

Discrete data

This is data that can only be identified sensibly by single whole numbers: for example, goals in a game, apples on a tree, books on a desk, amount of money in a pocket, number of pages in a book. All these data refer to whole numbers. For example, I cannot score 2.8 goals in a game (though this could be an average or other derived score).

Continuous data

This is data that cannot be measured exactly but is given as rounded-off numbers: for example, height, weight, age, speed. You always give these items as a rounded-off number such as 160 cm, 32 kg, 3 years, 30 m.p.h. You cannot be exact, but you can be very close by *rounding*.

DATA COLLECTION SHEET

This is a sheet used to collect data so that it can be processed later. It often takes the form of a *tally* sheet that is filled in after asking a question or making an observation.

Example

On which day do you want to have a school outing? Design a data collection sheet that can help you to decide which day is best.

On which day do you want to have a school outing?		
Day of the week	Tally	Frequency
Monday	⊥⊥⊥⊥ ⊥⊥⊥⊥ 11	12
Tuesday	⊥⊥⊥⊥ 11	7
Wednesday	⊥⊥⊥⊥ ⊥⊥⊥⊥ ⊥⊥⊥⊥ 111	18
Thursday	⊥⊥⊥⊥ 111	8
Friday	⊥⊥⊥⊥ ⊥⊥⊥⊥ 11	12
Saturday	⊥⊥⊥⊥ ⊥⊥⊥⊥	10
Sunday	111	3
Total		70

From this data collection sheet a decision can now be made.

Example KS3 question

The cook at a school wishes to provide more vegetarian food during one school term. For four weeks all the food will be vegetarian. Here are five suggestions as to what may happen:

1 Fewer people will have school dinners.

2 More older pupils will have school dinners.

3 More girls than before will have school dinners.

4 More teachers will have school dinners.

5 At first fewer people will have school dinners, but eventually more would have them when they heard how good they were.

The cook made an observation sheet so that she could monitor what happened before, during and after the four week trial as necessary.

Day of the week	Female/male	Pupil/teacher
Mon/Tue/Wed/Thu/Fri		

(a) (i) Which of the five suggestions *cannot* be tested by the observation sheet?

 (ii) Provide one more heading for the observation sheet that would help the cook to test this (missing) suggestion.

(b) (i) At what times might the observation sheet be used if it is to test suggestion 5?

 (ii) Improve one of the column headings on the sheet so that it can be used to test suggestion 5.

(c) How can we tell if suggestion 1 is right?

Solution

(a) (i) Suggestion 2 talks about older pupils, and the sheet has no reference to age at all.

 (ii) If a new column heading 'pupil year' was used, then suggestion 2 could now be tested.

(b) (i) Since the suggestion talks about 'at first', the sheet should be used before the trial starts and used again at the end of the four week trial, maybe yet again several weeks after the trial has finished.

 (ii) You really need to check this suggestion every day of the four week trial period, and perhaps for several weeks after the trial has finished. So if another heading for 'week' or 'date' was presented, you would gather data from every day of each week.

(c) By making observations before the trial, during the trial and after the trial to see what happens to the numbers eating school dinners.

DECAGON

A decagon is a ten sided *polygon.* Its inside (interior) angles add up to $(10–2) \times 180° = 1440°.$

A *regular* decagon (Figure D.1) will have ten sides of equal length. Its **interior angles** will be equal at 144° and its **exterior angles** equal at 36°. It will have ten **lines of symmetry** and will have **rotational symmetry** of order ten.

 polygon

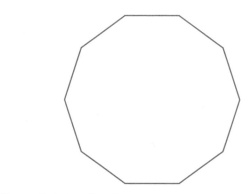

Figure D.1 Regular decagon

DECIMAL PLACES

The decimal places are the places to the right of the decimal point.

23.7   has *one* decimal place
23.54   has *two* decimal places
23.198   has *three* decimal places, etc.

You round numbers off to a given number of decimal places by using the following rules:

● Say you want to round off to two decimal places.

● Look at the number in the third decimal place.

● If it is less than 5, then the two decimal places remain the same.

● If it is 5 or more than 5 then think of the first two decimal place numbers as together forming a number between 1 and 99, and then add 1 to this. This new number now represents your two decimal places.

Examples

● 9.5427 will round to 9.54 (the 2 of the third decimal place is less than 5, so we keep 54).

● 11.1873 will round to 11.19 (the 7 of the third decimal place is more than 5, so we need to add 1 to 18, making 19).

● 23.6154 will round to 23.62 (the 5 of the third decimal place causes us to add 1 to 61, making 62).

| Number | Decimal places for rounding | | |
	1	2	3
13.6537	13.7	13.65	13.654
0.0593	0.1	0.06	0.059
6.3972	6.4	6.40	6.397

This idea of **rounding** off to a certain number of decimal places causes many problems and mistakes. Look at the table above to check your understanding.

 *rounding*

DECIMALS

This is the name generally given to all those numbers with *decimal places* in them. The **decimal point** separates the whole numbers from the fractions of numbers.

There are two types of decimal numbers.

Recurring decimals

These are decimals that go on and on and on, following the same pattern. We use dots to indicate the pattern. For example,

$$0.333\ 333\ 333\ 33... = 0.\dot{3}$$

$$7.181\ 818\ 181\ 818... = 7.\dot{1}\dot{8}$$

$$3.143\ 143\ 143\ 143.... = 3.\dot{1}4\dot{3}$$

You can find many more recurring decimals for yourself by changing fractions into decimals. To change a fraction into a decimal all you have to do is to divide the top number by the bottom number on your calculator (don't forget to press =). Try changing 1/3, 2/9, 3/7, 4/11, 5/13 and many other fractions of this type. Now try writing them with the dot notation.

Terminating decimals

These are decimals that do not recur but stop after a certain number of decimal places: for example, 0.5 or 0.125.

You can find these terminating decimals from fractions involving 2, 4, 5, 8 or 16 on the bottom. Try some yourself, e.g. 1/5, 3/8, 5/16.

 *recurring, terminating*

DENOMINATOR

This is the correct mathematical word for the number on the bottom of a *fraction.* For example, in the fraction 3/5 the number 5 is the denominator.

DENSITY

This is a **rate**; it is the weight per unit volume. The units are usually given as grams per cubic centimetre (g/cm³).

Density is related to weight and volume, as can be seen in Figure D.2 which illustrates that:

$$\text{density} = \frac{\text{weight}}{\text{volume}} \qquad \text{volume} = \frac{\text{weight}}{\text{density}}$$

$$\text{weight} = \text{density} \times \text{volume}$$

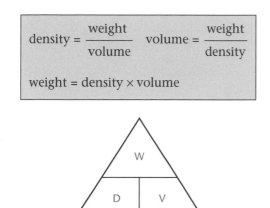

Figure D.2

> Note: Sometimes **mass** is used instead of weight.

Example 1
What is the density of a bar of metal that weighs 3.44 kg and has a volume of 400 cm³?

$$\text{density} = \frac{\text{weight}}{\text{volume}} = \frac{3440}{400} \text{ g/cm}^3 = 8.6 \text{ g/cm}^3$$

Example 2
What is the weight of 350 cm³ of a metal with a density of 7.2 g/cm³?

$$\text{weight} = \text{volume} \times \text{density} = 350 \times 7.2 = 2520 \text{ g} = 2.52 \text{ kg}$$

Example 3
What is the volume of a piece of plastic with a density of 1.8 g/cm³, weighing 260 g?

$$\text{volume} = \frac{\text{weight}}{\text{density}} = \frac{260}{1.8} = 144.4 \text{ cm}^3 \text{ (rounded)}$$

> Warning: be careful with the units, as we have in the above examples.

DIAGONAL

A diagonal is a straight line from one corner of a **polygon** to another. The dashed lines in the polygon in Figure D.3 are all the diagonals from one point A.

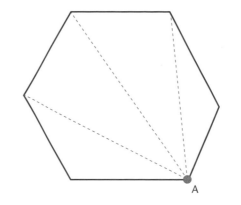

Figure D.3

DIAMETER

A diameter is a line that passes through the centre of a **circle** and goes from one side of the **circumference** to the other side of the circumference (Figure D.4).

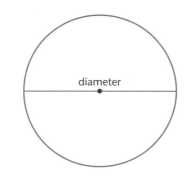

diameter

Figure D.4

 circle, circumference

DIGIT

A digit is a single item in a number. For example, the number 34 has two digits, 3 and 4, whereas the number 618 has three digits, 6, 1 and 8.

DIRECT

A direct relationship is where two (or more) variables move in the same direction. This is sometimes known as a positive correlation between variables.

 correlation, proportion

DIRECTED NUMBERS

This is the term often used for numbers when we are dealing with positive and negative numbers.

Look at the number line in Figure D.5.

The 0 is in the middle. All numbers to the right of this 0 are the **positive** numbers, and all those to the left of the 0 are the **negative** numbers.

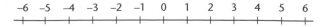

Figure D.5 Number line

Negative numbers are sometimes called minus numbers, because they are written with a minus sign in front of them.

There are some rules about directed numbers that you will need to be familiar with.

Adding and subtracting

- When we *add* a *positive* number, we always move towards the right on the number line. Check these examples in Figure D.6:

  $2 + 3 = 5$
  $-3 + 5 = 2$
  $-5 + 4 = -1$

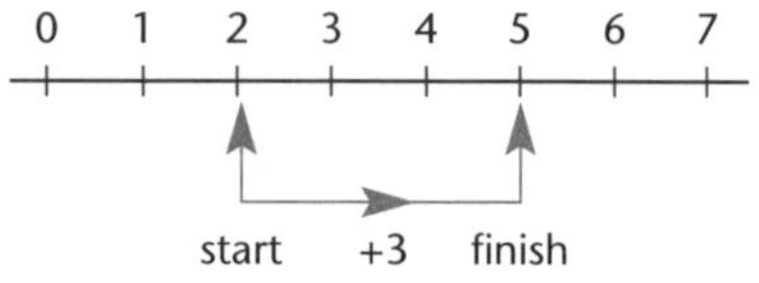

(a) $2 + 3 = 5$

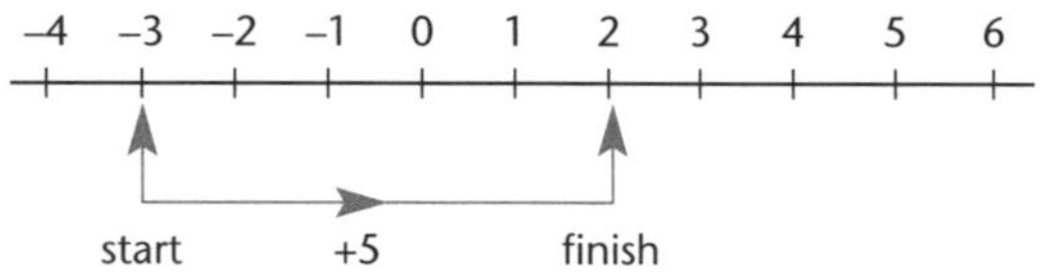

(b) $-3 + 5 = 2$

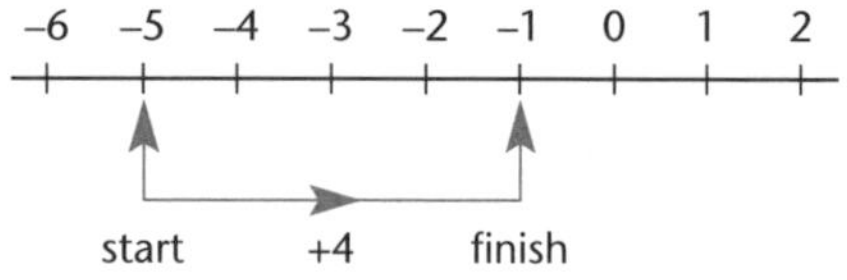

(c) $-5 + 4 = -1$

Figure D.6

- When we *subtract* a *positive* number, we always move towards the left on the number line. Check these examples in Figure D.7:

  $6 - 2 = 4$
  $-2 - 3 = -5$

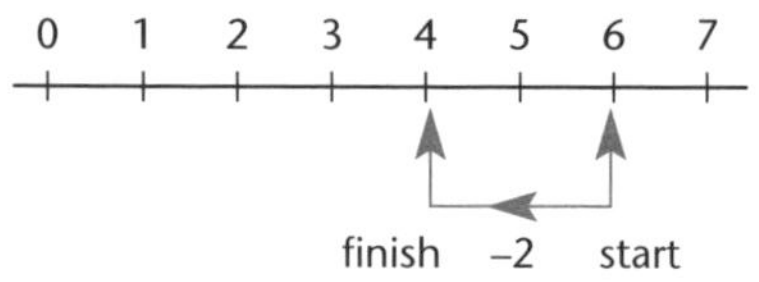

(a) $6 - 2 = 4$

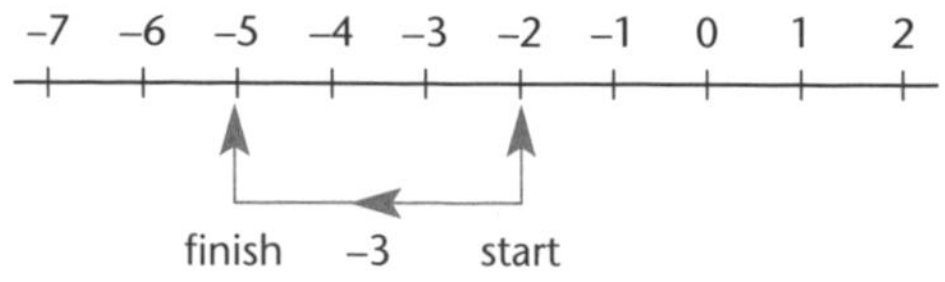

(b) $-2 - 3 = -5$

Figure D.7

- When we *add* a *negative* number, it is the same as subtracting a positive number: we always move towards the left on the number line. Check these examples in Figure D.8:

  $3 + -2 = 1$
  $-1 + -3 = -4$

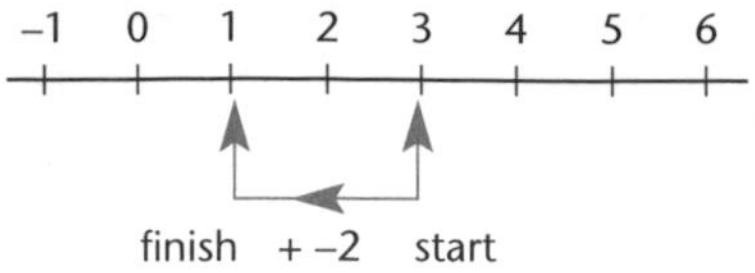

(a) $3 + -2 = 1$

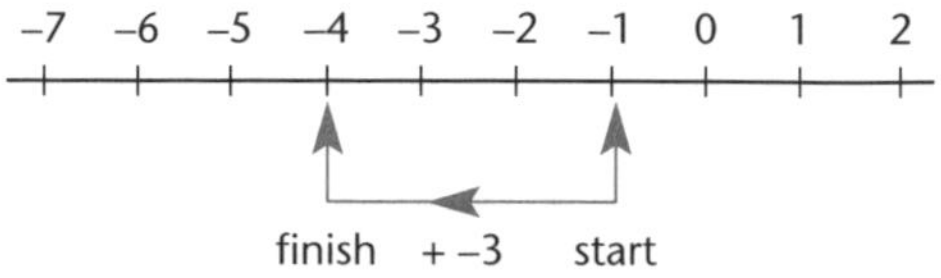

(b) $-1 + -3 = -4$

Figure D.8

- When we *subtract* a *negative* number, it is the same as adding a positive number: we always move towards the right on the number line. Check these examples in Figure D.9:

  $3 - -2 = 5$
  $-6 - -4 = -2$
  $-1 - -3 = 2$

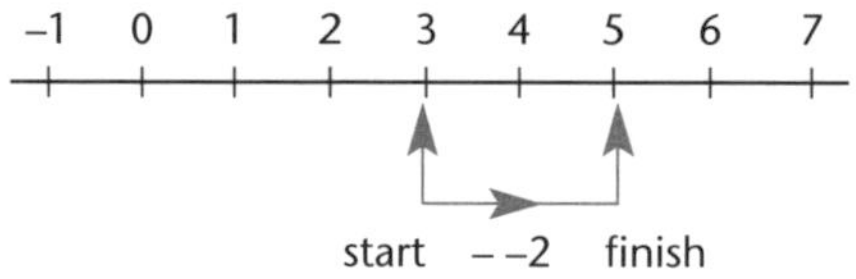

(a) $3 - -2 = 5$

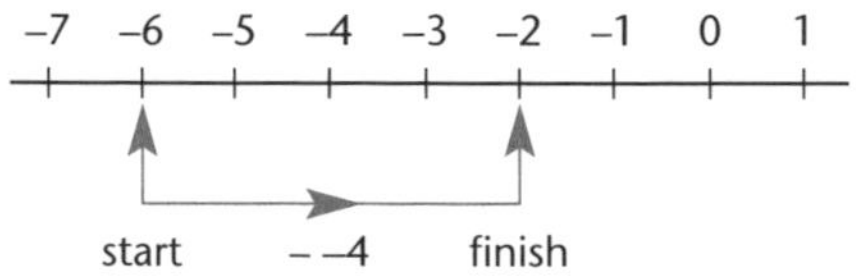

(b) $-6 - -4 = -2$

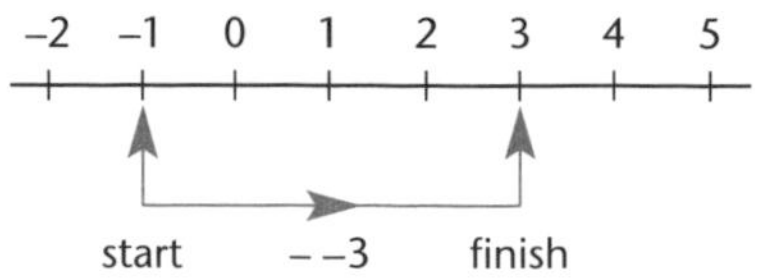

(c) $-1 - -3 = 2$

Figure D.9

Multiplying and dividing

When we multiply or divide directed numbers there are some simple rules for deciding what the sign of the answer is:

- If the signs are the same, the answer is a positive.

- If the signs are different, the answer is a negative.

Examples

$2 \times 3 = 6$ $-2 \times -3 = 6$ $8 \div 4 = 2$ $-8 \div -4 = 2$
$-2 \times 3 = -6$ $2 \times -3 = -6$ $-8 \div 4 = -2$ $8 \div -4 = -2$

Many errors are made by students working with directed numbers. Take time to learn the short rules and then use them.

DISCRETE DATA

Discrete data is data that is only presented in whole numbers.

-+- *data*

DISPERSION

This is the spread of *data* around its average.

-+- *inter-quartile range*

DISPLAY

Display is when information or data is shown on a diagram.
There are four main types of diagram presenting display data: *bar charts*, *pictograms*, *pie charts* and *histograms*.

Example KS3 question

A stall sells flags. In the morning it sells 5 red flags, 8 green flags, 4 blue flags and 7 yellow flags.

(a) Draw a bar chart to illustrate the data.

(b) Complete the pictogram in Figure D.10.

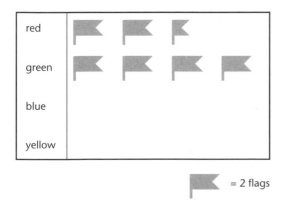

Figure D.10

(c) If you were to draw a pie chart, what angle would you use for the blue flags?

Solution

(a) The bar chart needs to be simply drawn and labelled, as shown in Figure D.11.

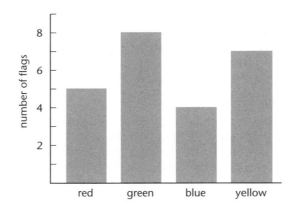

Figure D.11

(b) You must note the key, by which 1 whole flag represents 2 being sold. So the blue picture will need 2 flags to be drawn to represent 4 flags sold, and the yellow picture will need $3\frac{1}{2}$ flags to be drawn to represent 7 flags sold.

(c) The fraction of the total sale of flags made up of blue flags is 4/24. So the angle needed in the pie chart is that fraction of 360°, which is

$$\frac{4}{24} \times 360° = 60°$$

DISTANCE/TIME GRAPHS

These are *graphs* that illustrate a journey by plotting a series of points, as shown in Figure D.12.

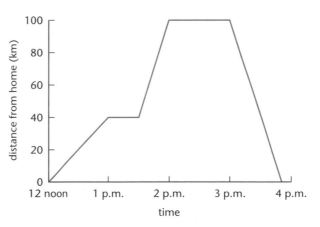

Figure D.12

The distance/time graph illustrates a journey from home by Hassan in his car, starting at 12 noon. At the start of the journey he travels 40 kilometres in the first hour, which gives an average speed of 40 km/h. He then stops for half an hour before travelling the next 60 km in half an hour, which is an average speed of 120 km/h. He again stops, this time for one hour, before setting off back home and covering the 100 km in 4/5 of an hour. This means that he travels at 125 km/h.
This last speed was calculated by finding the distance covered in 1/5 of an hour: 100 ÷ 4 = 25 km.

It follows that for 5/5 of an hour he would cover 25 × 5 = 125 km. Hence the speed of 125 km/h.

So you see you can get a lot of information from a distance/time graph.

Example KS3 question

Gordon and Nigel are two cyclists who compete in a race from Ashborne to Tellanby, and then back again. The distance/time graph in Figure D.13 shows their journeys. Point E represents a particular event in their race.

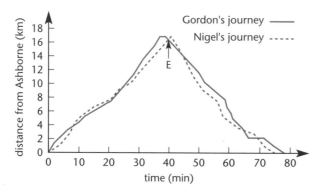

Figure D.13

(a) Part of the race was up a steep hill. Estimate, from the graph, the distance from Ashborne to the start of the hill.

(b) Two parts of Gordon's graph show a flat line. Explain what might be happening on these occasions.

(c) How many times did Nigel overtake Gordon?

(d) Describe what event is happening at point E on the graph.

Solution

(a) When they meet the steep hill, their speed will drop. At this point their lines on the graph will get less steep (shallower). This seems to happen at about 5 km from Ashborne.

(b) When the graph is flat, Gordon is not moving. At the 35 minute time he could be mending a puncture, and perhaps at the 65 minute stop he is again mending the same puncture. You can make up any sensible reason for what Gordon is doing, as long as you say he has *stopped*.

(c) You need to look at the graph for the dashed line showing Nigel's journey. Nigel is going further away from Ashborne on the outward part of the race, and is getting closer to Ashborne on the return part of the race. Where the dashed line is steeper than the continuous line, Nigel is going faster than Gordon, and is therefore overtaking him. This happens at 8 minutes, 44 minutes and 70 minutes. So Nigel overtakes Gordon three times in this race.

(d) At E, Nigel is still travelling away from Ashborne, but Gordon is now on his way back to Ashborne. So they will pass each other in opposite directions.

✦ *graphs, travel graphs*

DIVIDING

The symbol for dividing is usually ÷, but the use of fraction notation also means divide, e.g. 3/4 means 3 divided by 4.

Most division can be done using your *calculator*, and then perhaps *rounding* off the answer. But you do need to be able to do division without a calculator (although it is sensible to check with a calculator in an exam). This will fall into the two types, simple and long.

Simple division

For example,

940 ÷ 4

There are quite a few ways to do this, one of which is to set it out as follows:

```
      2 3 5
  4 | 9 ¹4 ²0
```

● We divide the 4 into the 9 first, to get 2 remainder 1. The 1 is put next to the 4 to give 14.

● Next we divide 4 into the 14 to give 3 remainder 2. The 2 is put next to the 0 to make 20.

● Finally we divide the 20 by 4 to get 5.

● Our answer will be 940 ÷ 4 = 235.

Long division

This is more messy. It involves dividing by a number bigger than 10. For example,

809 ÷ 23

Again there are many different ways to do this, but the traditional way of doing long division is as follows:

```
          3 5
    23 | 809
         69
        ----
         119
         115
        ----
           4
```

● We could start by asking how many 23s there are in 80. We can work out that it must be 3.

- So we multiply 23 by 3, putting the answer 69 under the 80.

- Now take 69 away from 80 to give 11, and bring down the 9 to give 119.

- We now ask how many 23s there are in 119. We can see it will be 5.

- So we multiply 23 by 5 to get 115, put this under the 119 and take away.

- We get 4, which is the remainder since there is nothing left to bring down.

- Our answer will be 809 ÷ 23 = 35 remainder 4.

Look out for the signs or instructions in your tests telling you when *not* to use a calculator. It is then important that you show how you did your division without a calculator.

Example KS3 question

A small chocolate bar costs 8p. Kieron has 98p in his pocket. How many chocolate bars can he buy with 98p? (*Do not* use a calculator.)

Solution

You are asked *not* to use a calculator, so you *must* show some working to convince someone that you have not used the calculator. Do a simple division as follows:

$$\begin{array}{r} 1 \quad 2 \quad \text{r.2} \\ 8 \overline{\smash{)}9 \; {}^{1}8} \end{array}$$

- The small 1 to the left of the 8 in 98 shows that you have divided 9 by 8 and got 1 remainder 1.

- r.2 shows that you have divided 18 by 8 and got 2 remainder 2.

> *All this is good evidence that you have **not** used your calculator.*

- The answer then is 12 chocolate bars (with 2p left over).

> *Once you have found an answer, it would be wise to check it on your calculator so that if you are wrong then you can look and see where you went wrong.*

- So check 98 ÷ 8 = 12.25. Yes, my calculator tells me that my answer of 12 is correct.

DIVISION

-+- *dividing*

DIVISOR

This is the proper mathematical word for the number you are dividing by.

DODECAGON

This is a polygon with twelve sides.

-+- *polygon*

DRAWING

- You may have to draw an **angle**. Use a protractor and a sharp pencil.

- You may have to draw a **graph** or a **chart**. Use sharp pencils and be sure to work out how big you need it *before* you start drawing anything.

- You may have to draw a **shape** on square or isometric paper. Be sure to think carefully about showing all the seen sides; the hidden sides can be shown by dashed lines.

Example KS3 question

A sketch of a net for a triangular prism is shown in Figure D.14.

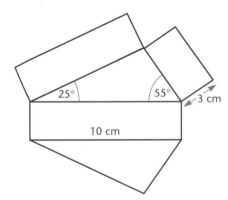

Figure D.14

Draw accurately the whole net.

Solution

- Draw the middle triangle first. Start with the base of 10 cm and then put each angle on the end.

- Now you can draw a rectangle on each side of the triangle with a height of 3 cm.

- Finish by drawing another triangle, the same size as the first but upside-down.

-+- *construct, net*

EDGE

An edge is where two faces meet in a three dimensional shape (Figure E.1).

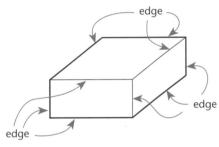

Figure E.1

ENLARGEMENT

The idea of an enlargement is to make a shape bigger. Look how it is done in mathematics using two different methods.

Method 1

We start with a shape and a centre of enlargement (Figure E.2).

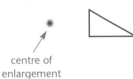

Figure E.2

Lines are then drawn from the centre of enlargement to each point on the shape, and extended beyond those points (Figure E.3).

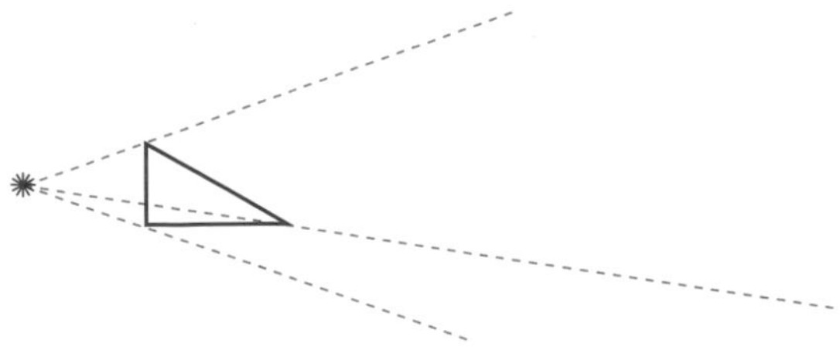

Figure E.3

Then you need a *scale* factor; this tells you how many times bigger than the original shape you want the new shape to be. If the scale factor is three:

- Measure the distance from the centre of enlargement to each point on the shape.
- Multiply this by three.
- Then find the point exactly that distance away from the centre of enlargement along the extended line you have just drawn (Figure E.4).

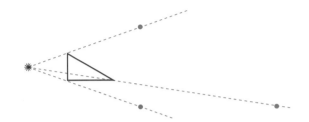

Figure E.4

- Join up all the new points you have found in this way. This will give you your new enlarged shape (Figure E.5).

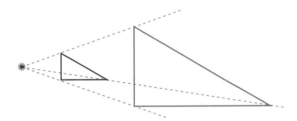

Figure E.5 Enlargement with scale factor 3, and centre of enlargement

Method 2

This doesn't have a centre of enlargement. Here you simply draw the new shape with all the sides bigger than the original.

So if you were to enlarge the rectangle in Figure E.6a with a scale factor of three, then the new shape would have all its sides three times bigger than the original. This is shown in Figure E.6b.

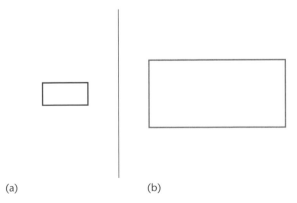

(a)   (b)

Figure E.6 Enlargement with scale factor 3 and no centre of enlargement

The difference between the two methods is that method 1 uses a centre of enlargement and the enlarged shape will have to be in one particular place. In method 2, with no centre of enlargement, the enlarged shape can be wherever you like.

EQUATIONS

Equations are what we might call mathematical sentences with an equals sign. For example, $3x + 7 = 13$ is an equation.

In an equation you will usually find just one letter that is standing in for a particular number, and you have to find that number.

An equation can sometimes have two letters standing in for particular numbers. In this case the solution will involve lots of pairs of answers that are usually expressed as *co-ordinates* and plotted on a line.

Equations with one letter

There are a few different types that you may meet. We discuss two.

Linear equations

These have no terms involving x^2 or x^3 or $1/x$. Examples of linear equations are:

$$x + 2 = 7 \quad 6 - 3x = 5 \quad \frac{3(4x + 1)}{8} = 5$$

We solve linear equations by moving all the numbers away from the letter, one at a time, using the following rules:

- First move the number that is furthest away from the letter (on that side of the equation).

- When the number is put on the other side of the equals sign, it does the opposite thing, i.e.

  + 3 will move to the other side to become − 3
  − 4 will move to the other side to become + 4
  × 5 will move to the other side to become ÷ 5
  ÷ 2 will move to the other side to become × 2.

- Carry on moving the numbers until the letter is on its own.

Example 1
Solve

$$3x + 5 = 11$$

(Remember that $3x$ means 3 multiplied by x.)

- Move the + 5: $3x = 11 - 5 = 6$
- Move the 3: $x = 6 \div 3 = 2$
- Solution: $x = 2$

Example 2
Solve

$$\frac{4x - 1}{3} = 9$$

- Move the 3: $4x - 1 = 9 \times 3 = 27$
- Move the − 1: $4x = 27 + 1 = 28$
- Move the 4: $x = 28 \div 4 = 7$
- Solution: $x = 7$

Quadratic equations

These involve squared terms, such as x^2. Examples are:

$$x^2 + 3x = 5 \quad 3x^2 = 15$$

The equations with only an x^2 term and no x terms can be solved quite easily by taking *square roots*.

Example 3
Solve

$$x^2 = 5$$

We simply take the square root of both sides of the equation (use your calculator for $\sqrt{5}$):

$$x = 2.24 \quad \text{and} \quad - 2.24$$

Notice that there will always be two solutions to equations like this, the positive solution and the negative solution.

The equations with both x^2 terms and x terms such as $x^2 + 3x = 4$, can be solved by *trial and improvement*.

Equations with two letters in them

These are equations of the type

$$y = 3x + 1$$
$$x + y = 8$$

They will always have a lot of possible solutions, in pairs. For example,

$$x + y = 8$$

has the following possible pairs of solutions:

$x = 8$	$y = 0$
$x = 7$	$y = 1$
$x = 6$	$y = 2$
$x = 5.3$	$y = 2.7$
etc.	

In fact there are millions of solutions, in only a few of which both *x* and *y* are positive whole numbers. Yet we can use these few pairs as *co-ordinates* and plot them on a graph, as in Figure E.7.

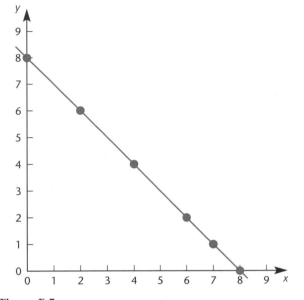

Figure E.7

Notice that for a linear equation we get the points in a straight line and can join them up.

⟚ *graphs, simultaneous equations*

EQUILATERAL

Equilateral means having the same lengths.

So an equilateral *triangle* is a triangle with all its sides the same length (Figure E.8). Notice also that its angles are all the same at 60°.

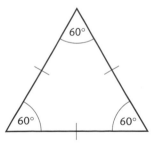

Figure E.8

An equilateral *polygon* has all its sides the same length but its angles do not have to be the same. Only if the equilateral polygon is *regular* will its angles be the same.

If the word 'equilateral' is used on its own, then it usually refers to an equilateral triangle.

EQUIVALENT

Two expressions that are equivalent have the same value but might look different. For example,

$t + t + t$ is equivalent to $3t$

$x \times x \times x$ is equivalent to x^3

Equivalent fractions

The fractions

$$\frac{1}{2} \quad \frac{2}{4} \quad \frac{5}{10} \quad \frac{7}{14} \quad \frac{11}{22}$$

are all equivalent fractions, since each will cancel down to $\frac{1}{2}$. You cancel down by dividing the same number into the top and the bottom of the fraction.

⟚ *fractions*

ESTIMATION

An estimation is a good guess at the length, weight or some other aspect of an item. It is usually made by reference to an amount already known.

For example, in Figure E.9 we can estimate the height of the lamp-post to be about 4 metres (12 feet), since the lamp-post looks twice the height of the man, and a man is usually just under 2 metres (6 feet) tall.

Figure E.9

EVALUATE

'Evaluate' means 'work out' or 'find the answer to'.
For example:

evaluate 3×4

means work out the answer to 3×4, which will be 12.

EVENTS

⟚ *mutually exclusive, probability*

EXPAND

'Expand' in mathematics means to multiply out the brackets.
For example,

expand $3(2x - 5)$

means multiply the 3 by everything inside the bracket to give $6x - 15$.

Quadratic expansion

If you are asked to expand $(x + 3)(x + 4)$ you need to multiply everything inside the first bracket by everything inside the second bracket, i.e.

$$(x + 3)(x + 4) = x(x + 4) + 3(x + 4)$$
$$= x^2 + 4x + 3x + 12$$
$$= x^2 + 7x + 12$$

Example KS3 question

Joy wants to work out $(t + 3)(2t + 5)$. She chooses to use the area of the rectangle in Figure E.10 to help her.

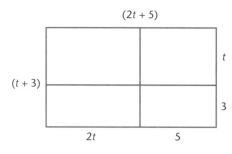

Figure E.10

(a) Show the area of each part of Joy's rectangle.

(b) Joy wrote $(t + 3)(2t + 5) = 2t^2 + 11t + 15$. Use the rectangle to show that Joy was right.

(c) Work out $(3p + 4)(p + 5)$.

Solution

(a) Each small rectangle has an area found by length × breadth. The areas are shown in Figure E.11.

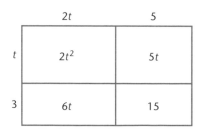

Figure E.11

(b) Add up the small rectangle areas to give:

$$2t^2 + 5t + 6t + 15 = 2t^2 + 11t + 15$$

(c) You could draw another rectangle and repeat part (b), or you could perhaps multiply the brackets out, with everything in the first bracket multiplied by everything in the second bracket. Either way you should get:

$$3p^2 + 15p + 4p + 20 = 3p^2 + 19p + 20$$

EXPECTATION

This is part of *probability*.

The expectation of an event happening is found as follows:

> expectation of event happening =
>
> probability of event happening × number of times event can happen

Example 1

The probability of it raining on a day in March is 0.35. How many days in March would you expect it to rain?

March has 31 days, so $0.35 \times 31 = 10.85$, which rounds off to 11. I would expect it to rain about 11 days in March.

Example 2

The probability of throwing the number 5 on a dice is 1/6. If I roll a dice 300 times, how many 5s would I expect to get?

The expectation is $1/6 \times 300 = 50$. I would expect to get about 50 number 5s.

> *Note: when we work out an expectation as above, it does not mean that we will get the number calculated. What it does mean is that we have a very good chance of getting an answer somewhere near that number.*

EXPECTED VALUE

✦ *expectation, probability*

EXPONENT

An exponent is the small number written at the top right-hand side of a number to indicate the *power* of the number.

An example is 3^4. Here 4 is the exponent and indicates that the four 3s are to be multiplied together, i.e.

$$3^4 = 3 \times 3 \times 3 \times 3 = 81$$

EXPRESSIONS

A mathematical expression is one which is found in *algebra*. It is simply a collection of numbers and letters.

All the following are examples of expressions:

$$x, \quad x^2, \quad 1/x, \quad x + y, \quad 5t - 3w, \quad \frac{3x + 6,}{x - t} \quad (x + 2y)^3$$

EXTERIOR ANGLES

Exterior means outside. Exterior angles are those angles found outside a *polygon* in the manner shown in Figure E.12. All the exterior angles in every polygon always add up to 360°.

In a *regular* polygon (all the sides equal) the exterior angles are identical. They can be found from the formula 360° ÷ N, where N is the number of sides in the regular polygon.

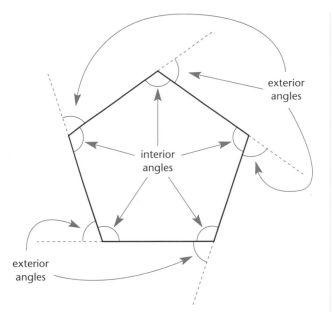

exterior
angles

interior
angles

exterior
angles

Figure E.12

✦ *polygon*

FACE

A face is a surface of a three dimensional shape (Figure F.1).

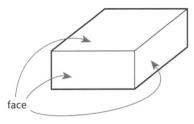

face

Figure F.1

FACTOR

The factors of a number are the whole numbers that divide exactly into it.

For example, the factors of 12 are 1, 2, 3, 4, 6 and 12 since each number will divide exactly into 12.

Prime factors

Every number can be written in terms of **prime numbers** (i.e. numbers which have exactly two factors). For example,

$$12 = 2 \times 2 \times 3$$
$$30 = 2 \times 3 \times 5$$

We refer to expressions such as $2 \times 2 \times 3$ as the prime factors of 12.

 prime

FACTORISE

When we factorise an expression we are separating the expression into **factors**. At Key Stage 3 we only factorise algebraic expressions such as $2p + pt$:

$$2p + pt = p(2 + t)$$

Here we have separated the expression into two factors, p and $(2 + t)$, which are shown as multiplied together. If you **expand** $p(2 + t)$ you will get back to $2p + pt$.

Here are some more examples of factorising:

$$5x + 15 = 5(x + 3)$$
$$3x^2 - 7x = x(3x - 7)$$
$$6t^2 + 9t = 3t(2t + 3)$$
$$6pm + pm^2 = pm(6 + m)$$

FIBONACCI

Leonardo Fibonacci was an Italian mathematician of the twelfth and thirteenth centuries. He was the first person to realise that the following sequence had a lot of remarkable mathematical qualities:

1 1 2 3 5 8 13 21 34 55

Each term is found by adding the previous two terms together.

This book is not the place to go into all the properties of this series, but try the following task. Put the series shown above into the following pattern of fractions:

$$\frac{1}{1} \quad \frac{2}{1} \quad \frac{3}{2} \quad \frac{5}{3} \quad \frac{8}{5} \quad \frac{13}{8} \quad \frac{21}{13} \quad \frac{34}{21} \quad \frac{55}{34} \dots$$

Now change each fraction to a **decimal** by dividing the top number by the bottom number. What do you notice?

Try continuing with the next few numbers in the sequence. What do you now notice?

 number patterns

FINITE

A finite number is a number that you can actually write down.

An **infinite number** is so big that you cannot write it down.

FLOW CHART

Flow charts are diagrams to help you work through a particular problem or sequence of events. They are extremely useful when writing computer programs, but we are not going to show this aspect here.

An example of a flow chart is shown in Figure F.2.

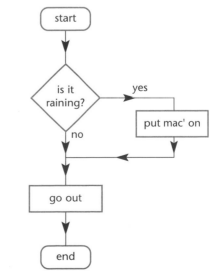

Figure F.2

35

As you see there are different shaped boxes. The conventions are to use:

- Oval boxes (Figure F.3a) as the start and end.

- Rectangular boxes (Figure F.3b) for instructions.

- Diamond boxes (Figure F.3c) for decisions where you go different ways for a yes or a no answer.

  (a) Start and end   (b) Instructions   (c) Decisions

Figure F.3

Example KS3 question

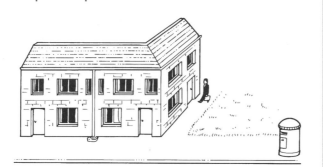

Figure F.4

Martin walks from his home to post a letter (Figure F.4). Then he walks back home again. The flow chart in Figure F.5 shows his journey. Fill in the empty boxes.

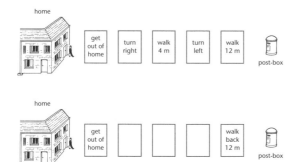

Figure F.5

Solution

You just have to think 'backwards'. The first thing he will do on walking back is 'turn right', then 'walk 4 m', then 'turn left' and he is back home. So your boxes should be filled in with these words, working from the empty box on the right to the empty box on the left.

FORMULA

A formula is a mathematical expression used to calculate something from other information.

Formulas (formulae) can be written in English or in mathematical algebra. For example, the area of a circle is found by multiplying π by the radius squared; or using mathematical algebra, $A = \pi r^2$.

You use a formula by knowing some information, substituting it into the formula and working it out.

Example

The formula for the cost £C of a trip of distance D km is given by:

$$C = 7 + 2D$$

What is the cost of a trip of 5 km?

Substitute $D = 5$ into the formula to get

$$C = 7 + 2 \times 5 = 17$$

So the trip would cost £17.

✦ *change of subject*

FRACTIONS

A fraction is usually part of something. However, this is not always true since you can have top-heavy fractions.

The best definition of a fraction is perhaps to consider it as the ratio of two numbers (or expressions) one on top of the other, for example

$$\frac{3}{5}$$

The top number (here 3) is the **numerator** and the bottom number (here 5) is the **denominator**.

There are two main types of fractions: **vulgar fractions** and **decimal** fractions.

- Vulgar fractions: these are the ones written as two numbers one on top of the other, e.g. 2/7.

- Decimal fractions: these are written as a decimal number, e.g. 0.245.

Here we are interested primarily in vulgar fractions, usually known simply as fractions.

Addition and subtraction of fractions

To add or subtract two fractions, change them to equivalent fractions with the same bottom number. Then we can add or subtract.

Example 1

$$\frac{1}{3} + \frac{2}{5} = \frac{5}{15} + \frac{6}{15} = \frac{11}{15}$$

We use 15 since it is the smallest multiple of both 3 and 5.

Example 2

$$\frac{7}{8} - \frac{5}{6} = \frac{21}{24} - \frac{20}{24} = \frac{1}{24}$$

We use 24 since it is the smallest multiple of both 8 and 6.

Multiplication of fractions

To multiply two fractions you simply need to multiply the top numbers and the bottom numbers of the fractions.

Example 3

$$\frac{3}{5} \times \frac{3}{4} = \frac{9}{20}$$

Division of fractions

To divide two fractions, you turn the second fraction upside-down and then multiply the two fractions together.

Example 4

$$\frac{2}{3} \div \frac{4}{5} = \frac{2}{3} \times \frac{5}{4} = \frac{10}{12} = \frac{5}{6}$$

Cancelling fractions

Example 4 illustrates the fraction 10/12 being cancelled down to 5/6 by dividing both top and bottom by the same number, in this case a 2.

Equivalent fractions

These are fractions that have the same value. For example, 1/4, 3/12, 0.25 are all equivalent to each other, and so are called equivalent fractions.

Example KS3 question 1

Shade 1/3 of the rectangle in Figure F.6.

Figure F.6

Solution

- If you measure the length of the rectangle, you will find that it is 6 cm long.

- Find one-third of 6 cm, which is 2 cm. Then mark a point 2 cm from the corner on one side.

- You can now draw a line straight down at that point.

- Shade the area to the left of this line, as in Figure F.7.

Figure F.7

Example KS3 question 2

Daniel and Liz share a pizza (Figure F.8). Daniel eats 3/8 of the pizza. A whole pizza contains 960 calories. How many calories does Daniel eat?

Figure F.8

Solution

You just need to find 3/8 of 960:

one-eighth is $\quad\quad 960 \div 8 = 120$
three-eighths is $\quad\quad 120 \times 3 = 360$

So Daniel eats 360 calories.

FREQUENCY

Frequency is the number of times something occurs. Frequency is often found by using a *tally* chart (Figure F.9).

blue	卌 卌 卌 卌 //
yellow	卌 ////
white	卌 卌 /
red	卌 卌 ///
green	///
other	卌 卌 ////

Figure F.9 Tally chart

Note how a diagonal line through four marks indicates a count of five.

Frequency table

This is a table in which the frequency is indicated.

Shoe size	Frequency
3	5
4	8
5	13
6	9
7	4

Cumulative frequency

This is often known as a **running total**.

Look at the following frequency table. The last column shows the cumulative frequency as the running total. See how it is built up.

Score	Frequency	Cumulative frequency
0–20	2	2
21–40	6	8 (2 + 6)
41–60	14	22 (8 + 14)
61–80	25	47 (22 + 25)
81–100	8	55 (47 + 8)

Frequency diagram

This is a diagram that illustrates frequency.

It could be a *pictogram*, a *bar chart*, or a *pie chart*. You could turn to each of these headings to see examples of what these frequency diagrams will look like.

A *histogram* is like a bar chart but has no gaps between the bars because the horizontal scale is a *continuous* scale. The dashed lines in Figure F.10 show a histogram.

↔ *histogram*

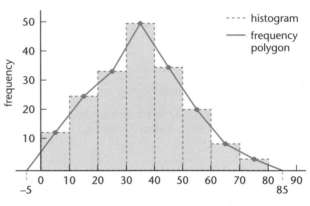

Figure F.10 Histogram and frequency polygon

Highlands

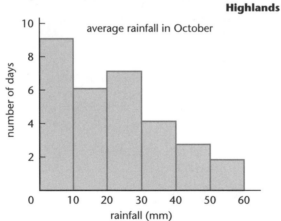

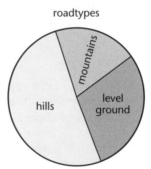

roadtypes

Lowton

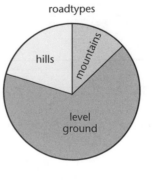

roadtypes

Figure F.11 Example Key Stage 3 Question

Frequency polygon

This is built up from a histogram as shown by the continuous lines in Figure F.10. We use straight lines to connect the *half-way* points of each rectangle of the histogram. We then extend these lines to the horizontal axis at each end, as shown.

Example KS3 question

Keith and Simon are planning a cycling holiday in October. They are trying to choose where to go, the Highlands or Lowton. They gather the information shown in Figure F.11.

Choose which place you would most like to go to for a cycling holiday. Use all the diagrams to explain your choice.

Solution

You need to bring each diagram into the argument, so you must mention both rainfall and road types for each place.

- Notice that the Highlands do not have as much rain as Lowton, in fact they have a lot less. Use the bar charts to make specific points of comparison: e.g. the Highlands have less than 30 mm of rainfall on 22 days in October, whereas Lowton has less than 30 mm of rainfall on only 9 days; and so on.

- Notice that the roads in the Highlands are nearly all hills and mountains, whereas Lowton is mainly flat. From the pie charts you can say that almost 3/4 of roads are hills and mountains in the Highlands, whereas only just over 1/4 of roads are hills and mountains in Lowton; and so on.

My choice would be the Highlands because there is less rain than in Lowton. There are also more hills and mountains which make it more interesting for the countryside views, even though it will be harder work to cycle there.

But if you had said, 'I choose Lowton because it's easier cycling as there are a lot more level roads, and I don't mind the extra rain that we shall get', then this is still a good, valid argument.

What is important here is that you interpret and *use* the evidence in the diagrams.

Frequency curve

If the half-way points at the top of each histogram are connected with a curve, rather than a straight line, then we have a frequency curve rather than a frequency polygon.

✦ *cumulative frequency, mean, median, mode*

GALLON

A gallon is an *imperial* measure.

Its *metric* equivalent is actually 1 gallon = 4.5461 litres. We normally use 1 gallon = 4.5 litres as a reasonable estimate.

GENERALISE

When we generalise in mathematics we are trying to show a *pattern* about the situation we see.

For example, in the number series

3,   6,   9,   12,   15 ...

we can see the pattern

1 × 3,   2 × 3,   3 × 3,   4 × 3,   5 × 3 ...

In noting this we are starting to generalise the situation, i.e. we have seen a pattern beginning to emerge.

The *n*th number

Often when we generalise we wish to be able to say what the 50th number in the series would be, or some other number well into the series. To do this we need to think about the 1st, 2nd, 3rd, 4th, 5th ... terms to see if there is a link between the number of the term and the term itself.

Example
In the series

4,   8,   12,   16,   20 ...

we can easily see the pattern

1 × 4,   2 × 4,   3 × 4,   4 × 4,   5 × 4 ...

So the *n*th term, where *n* can be any number, will be $n \times 4$, which is usually written as $4n$.

Spot the *n*th term

There is a simple rule you can use to find the *n*th term for any pattern where the numbers go up by the same amount each time. We call this amount the **common difference**.

To find the formula for the n*th* term:

- Multiply n *by the common difference: call this part (a).*
- *Take the common difference from the first term: call this part (b).*
- *The formula for the* n*th term is (a) + (b).*

Try to follow this rule for the following series:

5, 8, 11, 14, 17 ... : the *n*th term is $3n + 2$
7, 9, 11, 13, 15 ... : the *n*th term is $2n + 5$
3, 7, 11, 15, 19 ... : the *n*th term is $4n - 1$

You can check these solutions for yourself by substituting, say, $n = 3$ in each expression above. In each case the third term should equal 11.

More complicated patterns

Sometimes the pattern looks more complicated and you have to be more inventive to spot the pattern. Look at the following:

1, 4, 9, 16, 25, 36 ... :   the *n*th term is n^2
3, 6, 11, 18, 27, 38 ...:   the *n*th term is $n^2 + 2$

✦ *number patterns*

GEOMETRY

Geometry is the study of shapes, lines, surfaces, points and angles. There are lots of entries in this book which deal with particular parts of geometry.

✦ *transformation*

GRADIENT

The gradient of a line is its slope or steepness: the bigger the gradient, the steeper the line. In Figure G.1:

- **Positive** gradients slope upwards from left to right.
- **Negative** gradients slope downwards from left to right.

(a) Positive gradient   (b) Negative gradient

Figure G.1

To calculate a gradient

Create the largest *right angled triangle* that you can on a sloping line, so that the base is horizontal, the side is vertical and the slope is the hypotenuse (Figure G.2). The size of the right angled triangle is up to you, so choose the size that suits you best. Remember that the bigger the triangle, the more accurate you will be when finding your gradient.

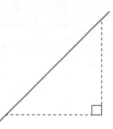

Figure G.2

Measure the distance along the horizontal and the vertical lines in your triangle.

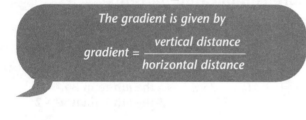

The gradient is given by

$$gradient = \frac{vertical\ distance}{horizontal\ distance}$$

Example 1

The gradient of the line in Figure G.3 will be 3/5 = 0.6.

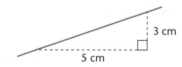

Figure G.3

Example 2

The gradient of the line in Figure G.4 will be –2/3 = –0.67.

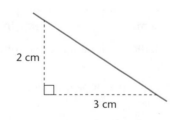

Figure G.4

Gradients on graphs

Finding the gradient on a graph uses the same approach: but take care in choosing your points. You should try to make the bottom number of your fraction an easy number to deal with.

Example 3

The gradient in Figure G.5 is 250/10 = 25.

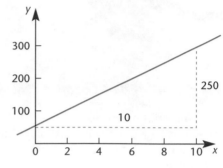

Figure G.5

Notice that we don't *measure* the actual length on the graph, but instead use the scales on the axes to tell us what length the lines are.

Example 4

The gradient of a distance/time graph will tell us the speed. On the graph in Figure G.6 there are two gradients and therefore two speeds.

● The first speed will be   300/4 = 75 km/h.
● The second speed will be   500/3 = 167 km/h (rounded).

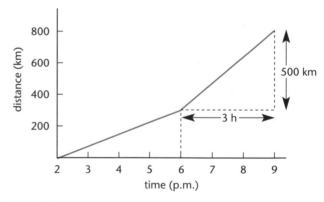

Figure G.6

✤ *graphs*

GRAM

A gram is a *metric* measure of weight.
    1000 grams are equal to 1 kilogram.
    450 grams are approximately equal to 1 pound weight.

GRAPHS

A graph is a visual picture of some data or information.
    There are *travel graphs*, conversion graphs and graphs from *equations*.

Travel graphs

These are graphs which tell us something about the distances travelled, the speeds and the times taken.

There are two types, *distance/time graphs* and velocity/time graphs.

Distance/time graphs

Figure G.7 is a typical distance/time graph. It represents a journey and shows the approximate times and distances away from base, say for a group of people in a car.

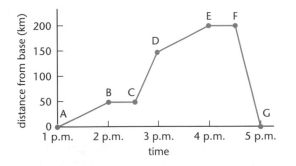

Figure G.7

The points are interpreted as follows:

- A represents starting from base.
- B shows that at 2 p.m. they are 50 km from base.
- C shows that at 2.30 p.m. they are still 50 km from base.
- D shows that at 3 p.m. they are 150 km away from base; and so on.

The lines are interpreted as follows:

- AB represents an average speed of 50 km/h.
- BC represents a stop for 30 minutes.
- CD shows an average speed of 100 km in 30 minutes which is 200 km/h.
- DE shows another average speed of 50 km/h.
- EF shows another stop of 30 minutes.
- FG shows getting back to base at an average speed of 200 km in 30 minutes which is 400 km/h.

The gradient of each line represents the average speed over that time.

Velocity/time graphs

Velocity is *speed* with a direction.
    Figure G.8 is a typical velocity/time graph. It represents the speeds of a particular journey. The graph is curved, but it could be straight.

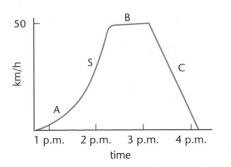

Figure G.8

- The curve at A represents the velocity increasing; we would say it shows **acceleration**.
- The line at B shows that a steady speed is maintained.
- The line at C shows slowing down or **deceleration**.

Conversion graphs

These are graphs that can help you to convert one unit to another.
    Figure G.9 can be used to convert degrees Centigrade to degrees Fahrenheit. Look at the graph to see how we have converted 25 °C to 77 °F and how we have converted 50 °F to 10 °C.

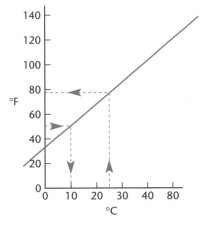

Figure G.9 Conversion graph: temperatures from Fahrenheit to centigrade

Graphs from equations

If you have an equation connecting two variables, then you can draw a graph to represent it.
    There are different types of *equations* which give different types and shapes of graph.

Graphs from linear equations

These will always be a straight line. You only need three points to be sure of your line.

Example 1
Draw the graph of $y = 3x + 1$.

Choose different values of x and see what the corresponding value of y is when you substitute the value for x into $y = 3x + 1$. We let $x = 0$, 2 and 4:

x	0	2	4
y	1	7	13

Plot these points on graph paper and join up the points to see the straight line, as in Figure G.10.

Every linear equation can be written in the form

$$y = mx + c$$

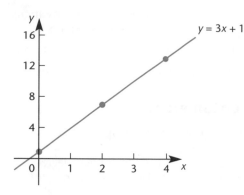

Figure G.10

If this is then graphed you will always find that m is the gradient of the line, and c is the place where the line cuts the y-axis.

Example 2

All the following equations will have parallel lines if they are graphed:

$$y = 3x - 4$$
$$y = 3x + 2$$
$$y = 3x + 9$$
$$y = 3x - 0.5$$

They are all parallel because of the 3 in front of the x.

Example KS3 question

Deva was investigating straight lines and their equations. She drew the lines in Figure G.11.

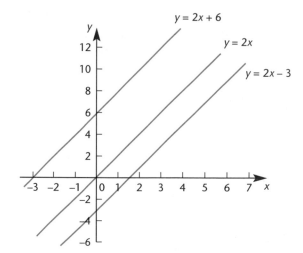

Figure G.11

(a) $y = 2x$ is in each equation. Write down one fact that this tells you about all the lines.

(b) The lines cross the y-axis at $(0, -3)$, $(0,0)$ and $(0, 6)$. Which part of each equation helps you see where the line crosses the y-axis?

(c) Where will the line $y = 2x - 18$ cross the y-axis? Write down this co-ordinate.

(d) (i) Draw another line on the graph which is parallel to $y = 2x$.

(ii) What is the equation of the line you have just drawn?

Solution

(a) Because they all have a 2 in front of the x, they all have the same gradient. So all the lines are parallel.

(b) The last number in each **co-ordinate** (with its sign) tells us where the line will cut through the y-axis. In other words it tells us the y-axis **intercept**. In terms of the general equation, the c is the part which gives us the intercept.

(c) Since -18 is the c in the general equation $y = mx + c$, the line will cut the y-axis at $y = -18$. Since at that point $x = 0$, the co-ordinate where it cuts will be $(0, -18)$.

(d) (i) You can draw any line on the graph as long as it is parallel to all the other lines, having the same gradient of $+2$.

(ii) The number in front of the x must be a 2, and the last number will be wherever you have cut through the y-axis. Put the two together for the equation of the line $y = 2x + c$, where c is the number on the y-axis where your line cuts.

Graphs from quadratic equations

A quadratic equation can always be written in the form

$$y = ax^2 + bx + c$$

The c is the same as in the linear equation: it tells you where the curve cuts through the y-axis.

Any graph from a quadratic equation will look like one of the graphs in Figure G.12, known as **parabolas**.

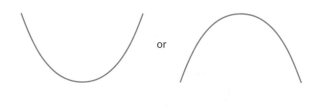

(a) Where a is positive   (b) Where a is negative

Figure G.12

Because of its shape you will need quite a few points to plot the graph of a quadratic equation. You will always be given a table of values, or at least the range of x values to choose from in order to find the points to plot.

> *Two important points to remember when drawing quadratic graphs are: draw smooth curves, and make them have a rounded bottom!*

Example 3

Complete the points in the table, then plot the points on the grid and draw the graph of

$y = x^2 - 2x - 3$. (The table is shown completed here; only the top row and left-hand column would have been given in the question.)

x	-2	-1	0	1	2	3	4
x^2	4	1	0	1	4	9	16
$-2x$	4	2	0	-2	-4	-6	-8
-3	-3	-3	-3	-3	-3	-3	-3
y	5	0	-3	-4	-3	0	5

This graph is shown in Figure G.13.

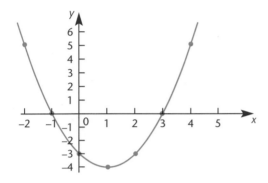

Figure G.13

Graphs from reciprocal equations

A reciprocal equation is of the form

$$y = \frac{A}{x}$$

where A is any positive amount. Graphs from such equations are called **hyperbolic**, but you need not remember the name until your A-level days!!

The shape is always like that shown in Figure G.14.

Figure G.14

As x approaches 0 it becomes impossible to plot values, since the closer x gets to 0 the larger A/x becomes. (Go on, try dividing 12 by some very small numbers like 0.000 03 and see what type of answers you get.) The same applies as y approaches 0.

Because of its complex shape, you would usually be given a table of values to use to draw the graph.

Example 4

Draw the graph of $y = 12/x$ for $-12 < x < 12$.

We can draw up a table of values (but not all those from -12 to 12).

x	-12	-6	-2	-1	1	2	6	12
y	-1	-2	-6	-12	12	6	2	1

Plot the points and you get the shape shown in Figure G.15.

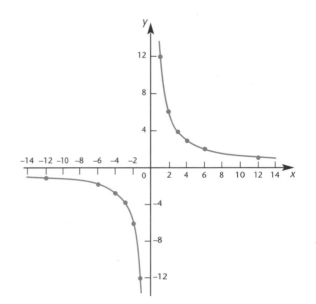

Figure G.15

GROUPED DATA

This is data that has been grouped. For example:

Height (cm)				
100–110	111–120	121–130	131–140	141–150
Frequency				
3	5	15	12	6

The data has been placed into groups of 10 cm. Notice there are gaps between the groups: this is because height is continuous and the data will be rounded off to the nearest centimetre.

Here is another example showing similar information, but using a different way of indicating the groups:

Weight w (kg)				
$100<w\leqslant110$	$110<w\leqslant120$	$120<w\leqslant130$	$130<w\leqslant140$	$140<w\leqslant150$
Frequency				
3	4	18	11	7

This time the *inequality* signs are there to say, for example in the $100<w\leqslant110$ group, that the weights are all bigger than 100 kg and are all less than 110 kg or equal to 110 kg.

HEPTAGON

A heptagon is a *polygon* with seven sides
(Figure H.1). It can also be called a septagon.

A *regular* heptagon has *exterior angles* of
360° ÷ 7 = 51.4° approximately, and *interior angles*
of 180° – 51.4° = 128.6°.

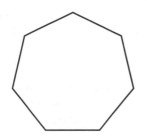

Figure H.1 Heptagon

Look at a 50p coin. It is a curved regular heptagon,
with the radius of each curve being the distance from
the opposite *vertex*.

✛ *polygon*

HEXAGON

A hexagon is a *polygon* with six sides (Figure H.2).

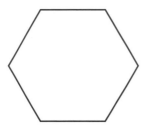

Figure H.2 Hexagon

A *regular* hexagon has *exterior angles* of 360° ÷ 6 =
60°, and *interior angles* of 180° – 60° = 120°. In
addition, a regular hexagon will show *tessellation*.

✛ *polygon*

HIGHEST COMMON FACTOR (HCF)

This is the largest *factor* that two (or more) numbers
have in common.

Example
What is the HCF of 18 and 30?

● The factors of 18 are 1, 2, 3, 6, 9, 18.

● The factors of 30 are 1, 2, 3, 5, 6, 10, 15, 30.

The highest factor to be found in *both* numbers is 6,
so 6 is the HCF.

HISTOGRAM

A histogram looks very similar to a *bar chart* but the
differences are as follows:

● A histogram will have a *continuous* scale.

● There will be no gaps between the bars.

● The area of the bars represents the *frequency* (the
  height does not necessarily represent the
  frequency).

Equal interval histogram

If the histogram has all its bars the same width, then
the vertical axis may well just be labelled *frequency*
(Figure H.3).

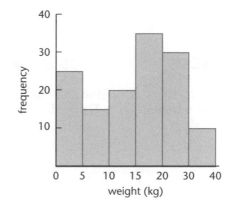

Figure H.3 Equal width histogram

Unequal interval histogram

If the histogram has unequal widths for the bars then
the vertical axis will be *frequency density* (Figure H.4).
The frequency is now found by multiplying the
height of each bar (the frequency density) by the
width of each bar.

To calculate the frequencies from Figure H.4:

Weight (kg)	Calculation	Frequency
0 < weight ⩽ 10	0.6 × (10 – 0)	6
10 < weight ⩽ 15	1.4 × (15 – 10)	7
15 < weight ⩽ 20	1.8 × (20 – 15)	9
20 < weight ⩽ 35	0.4 × (35 – 20)	6

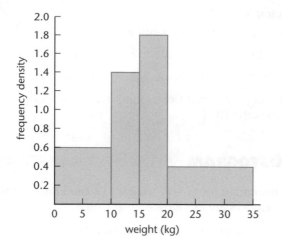

Figure H.4 Unequal width histogram

HYPERBOLA

A hyperbola is a graph of the form

$$y = \frac{A}{x}$$

where *A* is any positive number.

◆ *graphs, reciprocal*

HYPOTENUSE

The hypotenuse is what we call the long sloping side of a *right angled triangle*, as in Figure H.5.

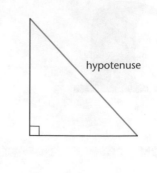

Figure H.5

◆ *angles*

HYPOTHESIS

A hypothesis is a theory. It is something you are likely to come across in statistics, and you may well be asked to prove or to disprove a hypothesis.

Example

'Tall people are better at maths than short people.' This is a hypothesis put forward by Mr Bean. Suggest how you can test this hypothesis.

To test the hypothesis you could draw a *scatter graph* of people's heights and their maths score in a test.

● If the *correlation* is positive then you can say the hypothesis is true.

● If the correlation is negative or there is no correlation at all, then you know the hypothesis is untrue.

IDENTITY

This is an expression which must be true for all values of the variables in the expression.

IMAGE

An image is what we use to describe the new points or the new shape we get after a *transformation*.

Example 1

In Figure I.1, the shape labelled B is the image of shape A after a *reflection* in the x-axis.

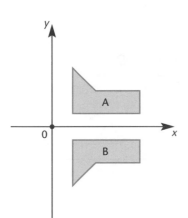

Figure I.1

Example 2

In Figure I.2, the points A′, B′, C′, D′ and E′ are the images of A, B, C, D and E after a *rotation* of 90° clockwise around the origin (0, 0).

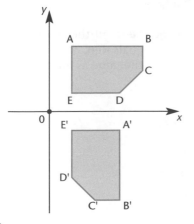

Figure I.2

✧ *reflection, rotation, transformation*

IMPERIAL

This is what we call the 'old fashioned' British units. For example:

● Length: inches, feet, yards and miles.
12 inches (in)   = 1 foot (ft)
3 feet (ft)   = 1 yard (yd)
1760 yards (yd) = 1 mile

● Weight: ounces, pounds, stones and tons.
16 ounces (oz) = 1 pound (lb)
14 pounds (lb) = 1 stone
160 stone   = 1 ton

● Capacity: pints and gallons.
8 pints (pt) = 1 gallon (gal)

For these quantities the imperial approximations to the *metric* system of units are as follows:

Length	Weight	Capacity
1 inch ≈ 2.54 cm	1 ounce ≈ 28.4 g	1 gallon ≈ 4.55 l
1 foot ≈ 30.5 cm	1 pound ≈ 454 g	
1 yard ≈ 91.4 cm	1 ton ≈ 1016 kg	
1 mile ≈ 1.61 km		

✧ *capacity, length, metric, weight*

INDEPENDENT

In *probability*, two events are described as independent if one event has no effect on the other one. For example:

rolling a dice   *and* tossing a coin
what you had for breakfast *and* the bus
                                                   coming late

The probability of *both* independent events happening is found by multiplying their probabilities together. For example, the probability of rolling a dice and getting a 5, *and* tossing a coin and getting a head, is found by:

five on a dice *and* head on a coin

$\frac{1}{6} \times \frac{1}{2} = \frac{1}{12}$

✧ *mutually exclusive, probability*

INDEX

An index is the little number that can appear on the top right-hand side of a letter or number. It represents the *power* to which that letter or number is raised.

For example, 3^2 which means three squared. The two is the index.

✧ *indices, power*

Standard index form

This is when we express a number as $A \times 10^n$, where $1 < A < 10$ and n is an **integer** (whole number).

✦ *standard form*

INDICES

Indices is the plural of *index*. Indices are *powers*, for example in x^2, 5^3, t^7.

● The numbers in the top right-hand corners are the indices.

● The letter or number raised to a power is called the **base**.

Rules of indices

As long as the base is the same for the indices then:

● To multiply, add the indices: $t^a \times t^b = t^{(a+b)}$. For example,

$$5^2 \times 5^4 = 5^{(2+4)} = 5^6$$

● To divide, subtract the indices: $t^a \div t^b = t^{(a-b)}$ For example,

$$5^7 \div 5^4 = 5^{(7-4)} = 5^3$$

● Any base with an index of 1 remains the same: $t^1 = t$.

● Any base with an index of 0 is 1: $t^0 = 1$.

INDIRECT

An indirect (or *inverse*) relationship is where two (or more) variables move in the *opposite* direction. This is sometimes known as **negative correlation** between variables.

✦ *correlation, proportion*

INEQUALITIES

These are the signs used to show whether something is bigger than, smaller than or equal to something else.

  $<$ means 'is smaller than'
  $\leqslant$ means 'is smaller than or equal to'
  $>$ means 'is bigger than'
  $\geqslant$ means 'is bigger than or equal to'

Inequalities on a number line

You need to remember the conventions in Figure I.3 about showing inequalities on a number line.

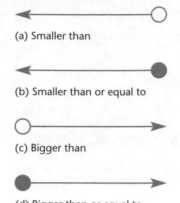

(a) Smaller than

(b) Smaller than or equal to

(c) Bigger than

(d) Bigger than or equal to

Figure I.3 The number line and inequalities

Look at the examples in Figure I.4 showing how we use the conventions.

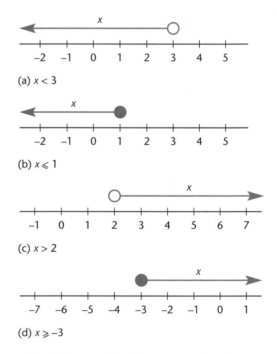

(a) $x < 3$

(b) $x \leqslant 1$

(c) $x > 2$

(d) $x \geqslant -3$

Figure I.4 Using number line conventions for inequalities

INEQUATIONS

These are like *equations* but they have an *inequality* sign instead of an equals sign. The rules for solving them are nearly all the same as for normal equations.

Example 1

Solve $2x + 3 > 8$.

$$2x + 3 > 8$$
$$2x > 8 - 3$$
$$x > \frac{5}{2}$$
$$x > 2.5$$

Inequalities involving square roots

This type of inequality requires a slightly different strategy.

Example 2

Solve $x^2 < 9$.

It is quite easy to see the solution $x < 3$ (by taking square roots of both sides).

But the *negative* square root possibility causes problems. It is *not* correct to just put $x < -3$, since that obviously gives the wrong answer. For example if $x = -5$, then this is < -3, but $x^2 = 25$, which is bigger than 9!!

What we have to do with the negative part is to change the inequality sign round to make sense of it. For example, in this case we say $x > -3$ (which you can now test to see if it works) in addition to the original $x < 3$.

In fact we normally put both parts together as $-3 < x < 3$. This can be shown on the number line as in Figure I.5.

Figure I.5 Number line solution for x² < 9

Example 3

Solve $x^2 < 25$.

This will have the solution $-5 < x < 5$.

Example 4

Solve $x^2 > 36$.

This example involves the 'bigger than' notation. We can see the obvious solution of $x > 6$ (just by square rooting) and we can get the negative solution by turning the sign round to give $x < -6$.

Together, this gives the solution $-6 > x > 6$. This can be shown on the number line as in Figure I.6.

Figure I.6 Number line solution for x² > 36

-⊹- *inequalities*

INFINITE NUMBER

This is a number so big that it cannot be reached by adding or by any other means. In other words an infinite number is too big to be counted. It is the answer to $x \div 0$, where x can be any number you like.

The symbol for infinity in mathematics is ∞. This is like the number 8 on its side.

INTEGER

An integer is the mathematical word for a whole number.

- Examples of integers are –126, –38, –5, 2, 6, 84, 1932, etc.

- Examples of numbers that are *not* integers are –3.7, 3.4, 0.5, 1/10, 10/71, etc.

INTERCEPT

An intercept is where a line crosses an axis on a graph.

- Where a line cuts through the x-axis it is called the x-axis intercept. This is the value of x when $y = 0$.

- Where a line cuts through the y-axis it is called the y-axis intercept. This is the value of y when $x = 0$.

If we look at the graphs that we get from an equation:

- Those in the form $y = mx + c$ will have the y-axis intercept at $y = c$.

- Those in the form $y = ax^2 + bx + c$ will also have the y-axis intercept at $y = c$.

-⊹- *graphs*

INTEREST

Interest is usually thought about in terms of money. It is the payment that banks and building societies give you in return for you lending them your money. It is also what we call their charge to you if you borrow money from them.

It is usually expressed as a **percentage**. It can be paid annually or every six months or sometimes even hourly!

Example 1

I had £45 in the bank for a year. They added 6% interest to the account at the end of the year. How much is now in the account?

6% of £45 is £45 × 0.06 = £2.70.
So the account contains now £45 + £2.70 = £47.70.

> *Note: it is easier to do the above calculation in one step as £45 × 1.06 = £47.70.*

Example 2

I kept £70 in the building society for three years. They added 8% interest to the account every year. How much was in the account at the end of the third year?

At the end of the first year I will have
£70 × 1.08 = £75.60.

At the end of the second year I will have
£75.60 × 1.08 = £81.65 (rounded).

At the end of the third year I will have
£81.65 × 1.08 = £88.18 (rounded).

It is worth noting that it will depend on which bank or building society you are with as to whether only the final amount will be rounded off or whether stages on the way will also be rounded off.

◆ *compound interest, simple interest*

INTERIOR ANGLES

This is the phrase used for the angles inside a *polygon*.
   The sum A of all the interior angles of an N-sided polygon is given by the formula:

$A = 180 (N - 2)°$

Example

What is the sum of all the interior angles of an *octagon*?

Since an octagon has eight sides we substitute $N = 8$ into the formula to give

$A = 180 × 6 = 1080°$

In a *regular* polygon (all the sides equal) the interior angles are identical. They can be found from the formula

$$\frac{180 (N - 2)°}{N}$$

where N is the number of sides in the regular polygon.

◆ *polygon*

INTER-QUARTILE RANGE

This is the difference between the *upper quartile* and the *lower quartile* found from a *cumulative frequency* diagram. In the distribution shown on Figure I.7, the inter-quartile range will be 30 m – 15 m which is 15 m.
   The inter-quartile range is used as a measure of spread (or *dispersion*) and is therefore very useful when comparing two different cumulative frequency diagrams. It is always given as a number and *not* a range.

Example

From a cumulative frequency diagram the lower quartile was found to be 13 and the upper quartile was found to be 28. What is the inter-quartile range?

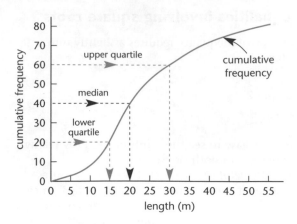

Figure I.7 Using the cumulative frequency curve to find the inter-quartile range

The inter-quartile range is 28 – 13 which is 15.

Semi-inter-quartile range

This is exactly half of the inter-quartile range.

INTERSECTION

This is where two lines cross each other. When two lines do cross each other, they create equal angles. As Figure I.8 shows, the intersection of two lines creates two pairs of equal angles. The angles that are 'vertically opposite' each other are equal and known as *vertically opposite* angles.

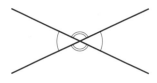

Figure I.8 An intersection and two pairs of equal angles or two pairs of vertically opposite angles

An intersection can also be used in the solution of a pair of *simultaneous equations*. This is found by drawing *both* graphs on the same axes and finding the intersection of the two lines.

Example

By drawing a graph, find the solution of the simultaneous equations

$2x + 3y = 8$
$y = 3x + 1$

The graph of each line drawn with the same axes is shown in Figure I.9.
   The solution is where the two lines intersect, which is at (0.45, 2.35). This gives the solution as $x = 0.45, y = 2.35$.

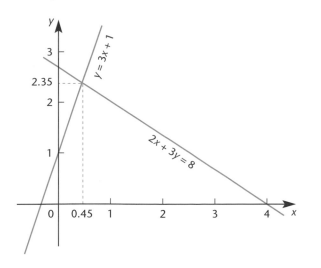

Figure I.9 Using an intersection to solve a pair of simultaneous equations

✛ *simultaneous equations*

INVERSE

An inverse relationship is where two (or more) variables move in opposite directions. This is sometimes known as **negative correlation** between variables.

✛ *correlation, proportion*

ISOMETRIC

You will only come across this in relation to isometric paper. Isometric paper is usually used to draw three dimensional figures, as in Figure I.10.

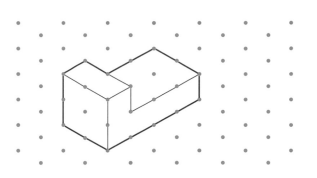

Figure I.10 Drawing a three-dimensional figure on isometric paper

ISOSCELES

You are likely to come across:

- **Isosceles triangle:** this has two sides of the same length, with the angles at the foot of each equal side being equal, as in Figure I.11a.

- **Isosceles trapezium:** this has the two non-parallel sides equal in length, with the angles at the foot of each equal side being equal, as in Figure I.11b.

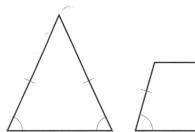 

(a) Isosceles triangle   (b) Isosceles trapezium

Figure I.11

✛ *trapezium, triangle*

Kilo

A prefix representing a thousand, used in the metric system of units.

Kilogram

A measure of weight equal to 1000 grams. It is strictly defined as the weight equivalent to the weight of a platinum-iridium cylinder kept near Paris. It is the approximate weight of 1 litre of water, and it is approximately equivalent to 2.2 pounds weight.

The unit symbol for the kilogram is kg.

Kilometre

A measure of length equal to 1000 metres. It is approximately equivalent to 0.62 of a mile.

The unit symbol for the kilometre is km.

Kilowatt

A measure of electrical power equal to 1000 watts.

The unit symbol for the kilowatt is kW.

Kilobyte

Used for computer memory. It means 2^{10} or 1024 bytes, where 1 byte is usually 8 binary digits or bits of either 0 or 1. It is loosely used to mean 1000 bytes.

1 kilobyte is shortened in the computer world to 1KB.

imperial, metric

Kite

A kite is a mathematical shape as shown in Figure K.1.

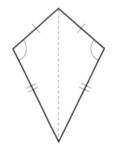

Figure K.1 Kite

- The top two sides are the same length.
- The bottom two sides are the same length.
- The side angles are both the same.
- There is one *line of symmetry*, straight down the middle of the shape.

LENGTH

Length is the distance from one particular point to another. The length of a rectangle is always the longest side.

Length is measured in terms of *metric* or *imperial* units.

Metric system

    10 millimetres (mm) = 1 centimetre (cm)
    100 centimetres (cm) = 1 metre (m)
    1000 metres (m)   = 1 kilometre

Imperial system

    12 inches (in)   = 1 foot (ft)
    3 feet (ft)   = 1 yard (yd)
    1760 yards (yd)   = 1 mile (mi)

System equivalences

The following expressions tell you the equivalence between imperial and metric length:

    1 cm ≈ 0.39 in   1 in ≈ 2.54 cm
    1 m   ≈ 1.09 yd   1 yd ≈ 0.91 m
    1 km ≈ 0.62 mi   1 mi ≈ 1.61 km

LIKE TERMS

Like terms in *algebra* are ones which can be added to or subtracted from each other.

Examples

x, $3x$, $-2x$, $5x$, $18x$, etc. are all like terms.
y^2, $3y^2$, $-8y^2$, $25y^2$, etc. are all like terms.
ab, $3ab$, $-7ab$, ba, $5ba$, etc. are all like terms.

x, x^2, x^3, x^4, etc. are all *unlike* terms: they cannot be added or subtracted.

LINEAR

Linear means straight. A linear line means a straight line.

A linear *equation* is one that gives a straight line when graphed. It is always of the form $y = mx + c$, where m represents the *gradient* and c is the y-axis *intercept*.

✤ *equations, graphs*

LINE OF BEST FIT

A line of best fit is the line that can be drawn on a scatter diagram to illustrate the trend (or the *correlation*) between variables. It is drawn 'by eye': that is, you use your *judgement* to draw the line showing the trend, trying to ignore extreme points and keeping the same number of points on either side of the line.

Note that the lines of best fit you will meet will almost always be straight, but they could be curved: compare Figure L.1a and b.

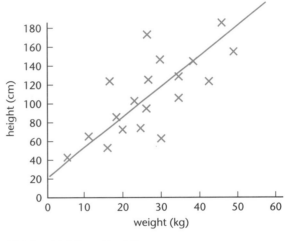

(a) A (straight) line of best fit

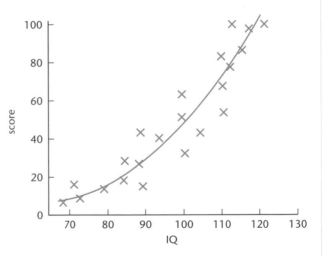

(b) A (curved) line of best fit

Figure L.1

✤ *correlation, scatter graph*

LINE OF SYMMETRY

A line of symmetry is that line which can be drawn so that one side is exactly the same as the other, i.e. a mirror image of the other.

Another way to recognise a line of symmetry is to imagine the shape folded along some line. Will one half of the shape then fold exactly onto the top of the other half of the shape? If it will, then the line is a line of symmetry; if it will not, then the line is not a line of symmetry.

Let us look at the parallelogram in Figure L.2 to illustrate this fact.

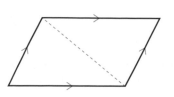

Figure L.2 Parellelogram

If you draw a dashed line from one corner to the opposite corner, as shown, then you do have identical shapes on each side of the line. *But*, if you then fold over the shape on that dashed line, the two halves do *not* lie on top of each other (Figure L.3). The dashed line is therefore *not* a line of symmetry.

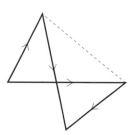

Figure L.3 Parallelogram folded along dashed line, showing that it is not a line of symmetry

Look at the examples in Figure L.4. These shapes do have lines of symmetry, which have been drawn in.

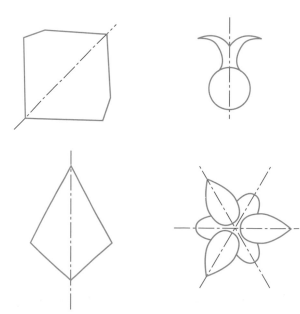

Figure L.4 Various shapes with their lines of symmetry

Note that a circle has an infinite number of lines of symmetry, so many that we cannot hope to draw them all in. Any diameter is a line of symmetry in a circle (Figure L.5).

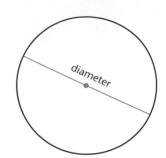

Figure L.5 Any diameter in a circle will be a line of symmetry

 symmetry

LITRE

A litre is a measure of capacity, that is a measure we would normally use for liquids. A litre is divided into centilitres or millilitres so that:

1000 millilitres = 1 litre
100 centilitres = 1 litre

● 1 litre is approximately equal to 0.22 gallons.

● 1 gallon is approximately equivalent to 4.5 litres.

LOCI

This is the plural for *locus*.

LOCUS

A locus is the set of all points that obey some particular rule.

Example 1

The locus of all the points which are 2 cm away from the dot labelled A is a circle of radius 2 cm with centre A, as in Figure L.6.

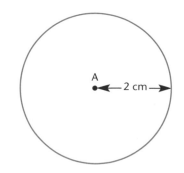

Figure L.6

Example 2

The locus of all the points which are 2 cm away from the line AB is the shape shown in Figure L.7. It includes two lines parallel to AB and a semicircle at each end (a racecourse shape).

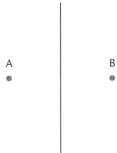

Figure L.7

Example 3

The locus of all the points which are the same distance away from two points A and B is the *perpendicular* bisector through the line AB, as in Figure L.8.

Figure L.8

Finding the pattern

To find a locus from a given instruction, we usually need to start by finding some points that seem to fit and then to look for a pattern that will account for *all* the points, as in the three examples above.

The most common mistake made by pupils doing a locus question is to predict the pattern too soon, without really thinking about what will happen at the corners or on the other side of the shape.

Example 4

Where is the locus of the points 1 cm away from the perimeter of a 4 cm square (Figure L.9)?

Figure L.9

The first set of points can be easily identified as parallel lines 1 cm from the sides (Figure L.10).

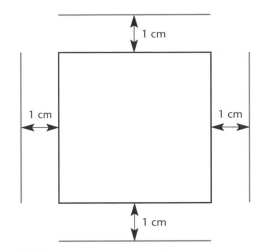

Figure L.10

What about the corners? Think back to the locus around a point (Figure L.6). Note that we have one point at each corner, so our locus at each corner will involve part of a circle. This can be drawn with a pair of compasses and is, in fact, a quarter circle at each corner (Figure L.11).

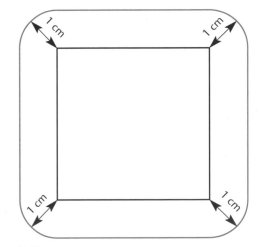

Figure L.11

What about inside the shape? Our locus will involve another set of lines 1 cm *inside* the square and parallel to the sides of the square. You can see from Figure L.12 that this means we will end up with a simple 2 cm square in the middle of the 4 cm square.

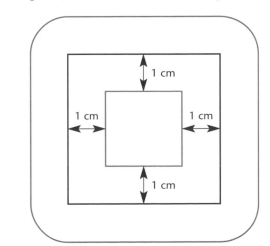

Figure L.12

Example KS3 question

Two goats, X and Y, are tied to opposite sides of a barn 4 m by 12 m, as shown in Figure L.13.

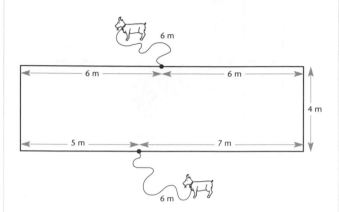

Figure L.13

They are both attached to the barn by 6 metre long chains. Draw a scale diagram to illustrate the area that each goat can reach.

Solution

You first need to draw a scale diagram, say of 1cm to 1 m.

The 'top' goat is the easy one. It will be able to reach a semicircle of radius 6 m.

The 'bottom' goat is more interesting. On the right it can reach a quarter circle, as it can on the left. However, on the left it can also get round the side of the barn!! At this point the chain gets caught on the corner of the barn. In effect it is now a small chain of length 1 m, so creating another, smaller quarter circle on the side.

Putting all this together will give you the area shown in Figure L.14.

LOWER QUARTILE

This is that value below which 25% of the total distribution lies.

✦ *cumulative frequency, quartiles*

LOWEST COMMON MULTIPLE (LCM)

The lowest common multiple is the smallest number that is a *multiple* of two (or more) numbers.

Example

Find the lowest common multiple of 6 and 9.

We list the multiples of each number:

● The multiples of 6 are 12, 18, 24, 30, 36, etc.

● The multiples of 9 are 18, 27, 36, 45, 54, etc.

We can see *common* multiples of 18 and 36 (there would be more if we had bigger lists). The smallest multiple is seen as 18, so the LCM is 18.

✦ *multiples*

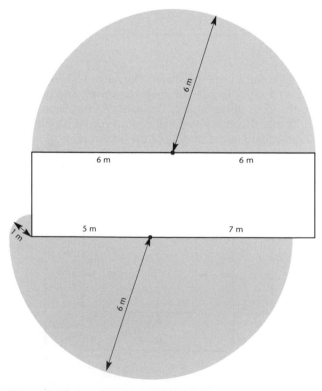

Figure L.14

MAPPING

A mapping is where we have some relationship between one *set* and another set.

For example, if the mapping is 'double' for a set of numbers {3, 4, 5}, this will map 3 to 6, 4 to 8, 5 to 10, etc.

✦ *transformations*

MASS

Mass is a word often used when we mean *weight*. The scientists will argue that mass is different to weight, and that is true; but as far as mathematics is concerned you will be able to regard mass as being the same as weight.

MATHEMATICS

This is the science of numbers and their possible combinations, including the use of letters for numbers in algebra. It also studies shape and space as well as probability and statistics.

It is often split up into **number**, **algebra**, **shape and space** and **data handling**.

MEAN

The mean is a type of *average*. In fact it is the most widely used type of average. Often it does not work out to be an exact number.

To find the mean from a simple list of numbers

Add up all the numbers, then divide this total by however many numbers you started with.

Example 1
Find the mean of 3, 7, 9, 2, 5, 6, 12, 3.

This is found by adding all eight numbers and then dividing the total by 8, i.e. $47 \div 8 = 5.875$.

To find the mean from a simple frequency distribution

We again follow the same principle, i.e. add up all the numbers and divide by however many numbers we started with. Since we start with the information in the form of a table, our solution will make use of another column in the table.

Example 2
The following *frequency* table shows how many eggs the 20 hens have laid overnight. To find the mean number of eggs per hen, we need to know how many eggs have been laid altogether and the total number of hens.

No. of eggs n	Frequency f
0	3
1	7
2	6
3	4
Total	20

The frequency table presents information in the form of the number of hens (frequency *f*) which have laid a particular number *n* of eggs. For example we can see that 3 hens have laid 0 eggs on that night, and so on. To solve for the mean we add a third column which multiplies each number *n* of eggs laid by the frequency *f* of hens laying that number. Adding all the values for $n \times f$ gives us the total number of eggs laid.

No. of eggs n	Frequency f	n × f
0	3	0
1	7	7
2	6	12
3	4	12
Totals	20	31

The mean number of eggs is given by:

$$\frac{\text{total number of eggs laid}}{\text{total number of hens}} = \frac{31}{20} = 1.55$$

To estimate the mean from a grouped frequency

We do not know the individual numbers in a grouped frequency, so we can only find an estimate of the mean and not the actual mean.

We make an estimate of the total for each group by assuming that everyone in a group is exactly half-way along a group interval. In the example below we can see that 3 people are in the group interval of 1–10 marks. Because of rounding, this group's interval is actually 0.5 marks to 10.5 marks, and half-way along it (the mid-point) is 5.5 marks. So here we assume that all 3 people score 5.5 marks.

Follow through this example involving a grouped frequency.

Example 3

A class of 18 students was given a spelling check and the number of correct spellings was summarised in the following grouped frequency table. Estimate the mean number of spellings each student got correct.

Group	Frequency f
1–10	3
11–20	8
21–30	5
31–40	2
Total	18

We construct additional columns to find the total number of correct spellings:

Group	Frequency f	Mid-point m	f × m
1–10	3	5.5	16.5
11–20	8	15.5	124
21–30	5	25.5	127.5
31–40	2	35.5	71
Total	18		339

The estimated mean number of correct spellings per student is given by:

$$\frac{\text{total number of correct spellings}}{\text{total number of students}} = \frac{339}{18} = 18.8 \text{ (rounded)}$$

Example KS3 question

This table shows how many seconds it takes using the Morse code to send each letter of our alphabet by means of a light at sea.

Letter	Sending time	Letter	Sending time	Letter	Sending time
A	5	J	14	S	5
B	10	K	10	T	3
C	12	L	10	U	8
D	8	M	8	V	10
E	1	N	5	W	10
F	10	O	11	X	12
G	10	P	12	Y	14
H	8	Q	14	Z	12
I	3	R	7		

In the table below are the six most frequently used letters in each of four languages, the letter with the highest frequency being placed first.

	English	French	Italian	Spanish
1	E	E	E	E
2	T	A	O	A
3	A	S	A	O
4	O	I	I	S
5	N	R	N	R
6	I	N	R	I

You might also read through the entries for *median* and *mode* before trying this question.

(a) Find the mode, median and mean sending time for the six most frequently used letters in *each* language.

(b) Which two languages are going to be the quickest for sending most messages? Explain how you decided.

(c) Samuel Morse invented the Morse code in his own language. Which one of the letters in the 'frequently used' table has a code which indicates that Samuel Morse's language was English? Explain how you decided.

Solution

(a) You need to replace each letter with its *sending time* in order to work out these averages. This gives you the following table of letters and times (in seconds).

	English		French		Italian		Spanish	
	E	1	E	1	E	1	E	1
	T	3	A	5	O	11	A	5
	A	5	S	5	A	5	O	11
	O	11	I	3	I	3	S	5
	N	5	R	7	N	5	R	7
	I	3	N	5	R	7	I	3
Mode	3 and 5		5		5		5	
Median	4		5		5		5	
Mean	4.7		4.3		5.3		5.3	

(b) Now look at all the averages. It would appear that French and English tend to send the quickest messages since they are the two languages which have the lowest means, and English also has the lowest mode and median.

(c) Each country has the letter E as the quickest and the most frequently used letter. Each country also shows the letter I in the top six most frequently used letters, and from this we can see that I is the second quickest letter to send. But English is the only language to also have the letter T in the top six most frequently used letters, and T is the second equal quickest letter to send. It is this letter T which indicates that Samuel Morse's language was English (he was an American artist and inventor).

✦ *average, frequency*

MEDIAN

The median is a type of *average*.

We find the median from a list of numbers by putting all the numbers *into order* and then finding the middle number. If there are N numbers arranged in order, then the median is the number in the $(N + 1) \div 2$ position.

Example 1

Find the median of 3, 7, 3, 8, 2, 5, 3, 5, 6, 8, 9, 12, 7.

- First rewrite the numbers in order, here lowest to highest:

  2, 3, 3, 3, 5, 5, 6, 7, 7, 8, 8, 9, 12

- Since there are 13 numbers we look for the $(13 + 1) \div 2 = $ 7th number. This gives the number 6.

- So, the median is 6.

Suppose there is an *even* number of numbers. The rule $(N + 1) \div 2$ gives us a *fraction* if N is even. In other words, there is no single number exactly in the middle of a list of numbers in order. But we do have two middle numbers, and the median is then found half-way between these two numbers. By adding the two middle numbers together and dividing by two, we get the median.

Example 2

Find the median of 8, 5, 7, 9, 4, 6, 7, 1, 7, 1.

- First rewrite the numbers in order:

  1, 1, 4, 5, 6, 7, 7, 7, 8, 9

- Since there are 10 numbers we are looking at the $(10 + 1) \div 2 = $ 5.5th number, in order, as the median number. This means we're looking at the 5th and the 6th numbers, which are 6 and 7, as the two middle numbers.

- We now add them together and divide by 2, which gives $13 \div 2 = 6.5$.

- So, the median is 6.5.

Finding the median from a grouped frequency

To find the median from a grouped frequency table you need to construct a *cumulative frequency* column and then draw a cumulative frequency diagram.

Example 3

Notice how the cumulative frequency column is found by adding the frequencies up to that stage. So up to 40 (strictly 40.5 with rounding) there are $3 + 7 = 10$ items altogether.

Group	Frequency	Cumulative frequency
1–20	3	3
21–40	7	10
41–60	19	29
61–80	11	40
81–100	5	45

The points are plotted as shown in Figure M.1. The median is the middle item, which is given by the $(45 + 1) \div 2 = $ 23rd position, in order. So find 23 on the cumulative frequency axis in Figure M.1, then go horizontally to the graph. Now go down from the graph to the values at the bottom. The median can then be read off the horizontal axis. By looking at the diagram, the median will be 55.

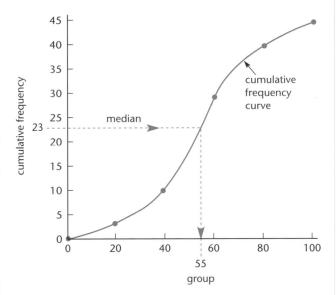

Figure M.1 Using the cumulative frequency curve to find the median for grouped data

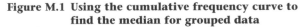

Note: since finding the median is only an approximation, many statisticians will say that you do not need to use $(N + 1) \div 2$, since $N \div 2$ is a good approximation to the median position, especially where N is a large number. It is therefore suggested that you use $(N + 1) \div 2$ for odd numbers and $N \div 2$ for even numbers.

MEGA

A prefix representing a million, used in the metric system of units. It can also simply mean 'very big'.

In computer use a megabit is actually 2^{20} or 1 048 576 *bits* (just over a million). A megabyte (MB) refers to the amount of storage within a computer system: it means 2^{20} *bytes*.

bit, byte

MENSURATION

This is the study of the rules for measuring *lengths*, *areas* and *volumes*.

METRIC

This is the measuring system originally based on the metre. It now refers to the systems that use powers of tens in their measurement. For example:

● Length:
   10 millimetres (mm) = 1 centimetre (cm)
   100 centimetres (cm) = 1 metre (m)
   1000 metres (m)   = 1 kilometre (km)

● Weight:
   1000 grams (g)   = 1 kilogram (kg)
   1000 kilograms (kg)   = 1 tonne (t)

● Capacity:
   1000 millilitres (ml) = 1 litre (l)
   100 centilitres (cl) = 1 litre (l)

➤ *capacity, imperial, length, weight*

MICRO

A prefix representing one-millionth, used in the metric system of units. It can also simply mean 'very small'.

● A microgram is one-millionth of a gram:
   1 000 000 micrograms = 1 g.

● A micrometre is one-millionth of a metre:
   1 000 000 micrometres = 1 m.

● A microlitre is one-millionth of a litre:
   1 000 000 microlitres = 1 litre.

MILLI

A prefix representing one-thousandth, used in the metric system of units.

● A milligram is one-thousandth of a gram:
   1000 milligrams = 1 g.

● A millimetre is one-thousandth of a metre:
   1000 millimetres = 1 m.

● A millilitre is one-thousandth of a litre:
   1000 millilitres = 1 litre.

MIRROR LINE

A mirror line is another word for a *line of symmetry*.

➤ *line of symmetry, symmetry*

MIXED NUMBER

A mixed number, as the name suggests, is a mixture of *whole numbers* and *vulgar fractions*. For example, $5\frac{3}{8}$ is a mixed number, where 5 is the whole number and $\frac{3}{8}$ is the fraction.

To change a mixed number to a decimal

Change the vulgar fraction part first, by dividing the top by the bottom. Then add the whole number.

Example

Change $5\frac{3}{8}$ to a decimal number.

First divide 3 by 8 to get 0.375. Then add the 5 to get 5.375.

MODE

This is a type of *average*. It is the item that occurs with the highest frequency.
   It is the only average that does not have to be numerical.

Example 1

Find the mode from the list:

   red, blue, yellow, blue, red, blue, white, blue, white, yellow, blue, black, red, blue

By counting how many times each colour occurs, you will see that there are more blue than any other colour, so blue is the mode colour. (We sometimes use the expression 'modal' colour.)

Finding the mode from frequency tables is easy, as you only have to see what the highest frequency is and state which item of data it refers to.

Example 2

Here is a table that illustrates how many children were part of the families attending the Christmas Service at a church in Banner Cross.

Number of children	Frequency
0	4
1	8
2	15
3	2

So the modal number of children will be 2. (The most common error here is to state the mode as 15, as that is the biggest number. Remember, always find the mode from the first column and never from the frequency column.)

When finding the mode from a grouped frequency table you do just the same, but this time you quote the *group* with the highest frequency.

Example 3

The following table shows the heights of the year 9 students at a school in Rotherham.

Height (cm)	Frequency
141–150	13
151–160	56
161–170	41
171–180	17

The modal height is 151–160 cm.

MULTIPLES

A multiple of a number is another number that can be divided exactly by that number. For example, 35 is a multiple of 5 since 35 can be divided exactly by 5.
   The multiples of any number come from their multiplication (or 'times') tables. For example:

- The multiples of 3 are 6, 9, 12, 15, 18, 21, 24, 27, 30, 33 ....

- The multiples of 5 are 5, 10, 15, 20, 25 30, 35, 40, 45, 50 ....

Common multiples

These are multiples that numbers have in common.

Example

List the common multiples of 6 and 8.

- The multiples of 6 are 12, 18, 24, 30, 36, 42, 48, 54, 60, 66, 72 ....

- The multiples of 8 are 16, 24, 32, 40, 48, 56, 64, 72, 80, 88 ....

So, the common multiples can be seen to be 24, 48, 72 and so on. We can see that these are the multiples of 24, so we could now continue the list of common multiples as far as we wanted to go.

Lowest common multiple (LCM)

This is the *lowest* of all the common multiples of two (or more) numbers. In the examples above, the LCM will be 24 as this is the lowest value of the common multiples.

✦ *lowest common multiple*

MULTIPLY

There is a set of rules for multiplying that you ought to know.

Rules for multiplying

$$\left.\begin{array}{ccccc} + & \times & + & = & + \\ - & \times & - & = & + \end{array}\right\} \text{ Signs the same: answer } +$$

$$\left.\begin{array}{ccccc} + & \times & - & = & - \\ - & \times & + & = & - \end{array}\right\} \text{ Signs different: answer } -$$

You can multiply two numbers together very easily on your calculator by using the × key.

Long multiplication

This is where you cannot use a calculator but need to calculate something like 364×53. Let's use this problem to show you how to do long multiplication.

Example

$$\begin{array}{r} 364 \\ \times \quad 53 \\ \hline \end{array}$$

1 0₁9₁2	from 364×3
18 ₃2₂00	from 364×50
19 2 9 2	adding the 1092 to the 18 200

Note: we have used the carry figures to demonstrate that we have done the problem without a calculator. In your exam, if you do not show these working-out figures then you will not get the marks for the answers. You can check your answers in the exam with a calculator, though, and this is recommended to give you confidence in the exam!!

Example KS3 question

(a) Estimate the answer to 124×28.

(b) Show how you made your estimate.

(c) Now work out the exact answer to 124×28 without using a calculator.

Solution

(a) The key word here is 'estimate': the question does *not* ask you to calculate the answer and round off!! So to estimate the answer, round off each number in the expression to one *significant figure*, which will give you $100 \times 30 = 3000$. So your estimate is 3000.

(b) You must *show* that you have rounded off *each* number to one significant figure. You get no marks for doing the multiplication on your calculator and then rounding off at the end!

(c) Now do the long multiplication, showing all the carry numbers:

$$
\begin{array}{r}
124 \\
\times\ 28 \\
\hline
9_19_32 \\
2\ 4\ 8\ 0 \\
\hline
3_14_17\ 2 \\
\end{array}
$$

from 124×8

from 124×20

> *Note that you do need to show all those carry numbers!*

MUTUALLY EXCLUSIVE

Two events are described as mutually exclusive if they cannot both happen at the same time.

Example 1

Rolling one dice, and the number on the top being a five and a three.

Both those events cannot happen at the same time; we would need two dice.

Example 2

Choosing a sweet from a bag containing toffees, jellies and mints, and the sweet being a toffee and a jelly.

The sweet cannot be both at the same time; we would need two different sweets.

Probabilities

If we have two events that are mutually exclusive, then we can be asked the question 'What is the probability of this *or* that happening?' When asked that question, we simply *add* together the two probabilities.

Example 3

A dice is rolled. What is the probability that the number rolled is a 4 or a 5?

- The probability of rolling a 4 is 1/6.
- The probability of rolling a 5 is also 1/6.
- So, the probability of rolling a 4 *or* a 5 will be 1/6 + 1/6 = 2/6.

Example 4

A game is played and you are told that the chances of landing on certain colours are as follows:

blue	red	yellow	black
0.26	0.18	0.34	0.22

You are close to winning and only need to land on red or black. What are your chances of winning on your next go?

The chance of winning is the chance of landing on red *or* black, i.e. 0.18 + 0.22 = 0.40.

✦ *independent, OR rule probability*

NEGATIVE NUMBERS

Negative numbers are numbers less than zero, for example those that appear below freezing point on the thermometer.

Negative numbers have a negative sign in front of them so that you can recognise them as being different from positive numbers.

There are useful rules for dealing with negative numbers:

- If you *add* two negative numbers together, you get an even bigger negative number: for example,

  $-3 + -5 = -8$

- If you *subtract* a negative number from a positive number, you are effectively adding those numbers: for example,

  $2 - -3 = 2 + 3 = 5$

- If you *multiply* or *divide* two negative numbers, you get a positive number: for example,

  $-3 \times -5 = 15$ and $-30 \div -6 = 5$

- If you *multiply* or *divide* two numbers, one positive and one negative, you get a negative number: for example,

  $-6 \times 4 = -24$ $-24 \div 8 = -3$

✦ *directed numbers*

NETS

A net of a *solid shape* is a flat shape that can be folded over into the solid shape.

Example 1

The shapes in Figure N.1 are all nets of a cube.

Look at each shape and visualise how each one will fold up into a cube.

Note: we do not normally draw the flaps on the sides that you would need if you were actually going to make the solid shapes.

Figure N.1 Nets of a cube

There is usually more than one way in which to draw a net of any particular solid shape.

Example 2

Sketch two different nets of a square based pyramid whose **vertex** is directly above the centre of the square base.

The nets are shown in Figure N.2.

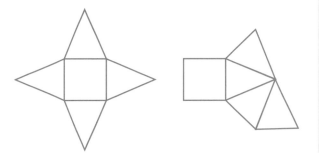

Figure N.2 Nets of a square based pyramid with vertex directly above the centre of the square base

Example KS3 question

(a) Which of the nets in Figure N.3 could be folded to make a **cuboid**?

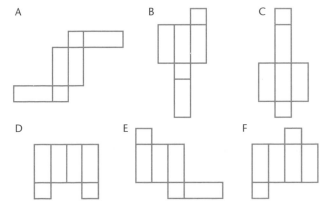

Figure N.3

(b) (i)   Which nets will *not* make a cuboid?
(ii)   Explain how you know they will not make a cuboid.

Solution

(a) You need to visualise folding the shapes up, one by one. The following shapes will make a cuboid: A, B, E and F.

(b) (i) The nets that will *not* make a cuboid are C and D.

    (ii) There are many different ways to explain why they do not make a cuboid. Here is one explanation for each net:

- C cannot because the 'top' and an 'end' are mixed up, so that you get the top on the end.

- D cannot because both ends are on the same end, so one end will not be there.

✥ *solid shapes*

NONAGON

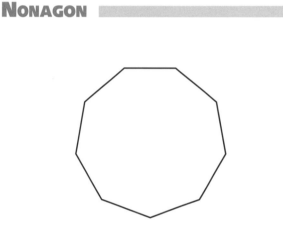

Figure N.4 Nonagon

A nonagon is a *polygon* with nine sides (Figure N.4). The sum of the interior angles of a nonagon is 1260°.

The *interior angles* of a *regular* nonagon (all sides the same length) will all be 140°, and the *exterior angles* will all be 40°.

A regular nonagon will have nine *lines of symmetry* and will have *rotational symmetry* of order 9. A regular nonagon will not show *tessellation*.

✥ *polygon*

NORMAL DISTRIBUTION

If you draw a *bar chart* or a *histogram* from a large population or sample involving variables such as weight or height, then you are quite likely to be drawing a normal distribution.

A normal distribution will have the kind of shape shown in Figure N.5. The majority of the distribution is in the middle, and the frequencies are the same on each side.

You do need a large sample to be able to get a normal distribution.

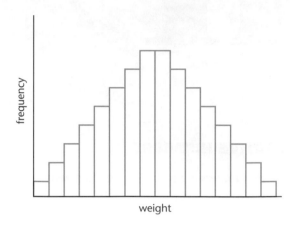

Figure N.5 Normal distribution (histogram)

NOT

The *probability* of an event A *not* happening is one minus the probability of event A happening.

Example

The probability of finding roadworks on the A1 is 0.72. What is the probability of not finding roadworks on the A1?

The probability of *not* finding roadworks is:

1 – probability of finding roadworks = 1 – 0.72 = 0.28

Example KS3 question

Pupils in a school like to watch these sports: football, hockey, basketball. The following statement might be made:

'The probability that the first pupil to arrive at school likes to watch basketball is 1/3, because there are three sports.'

This statement is likely to be wrong; explain why.

Solution

There are no figures given for those watching each sport, so we do not know that they are *equally likely* events. In fact it is probable they will not be equally likely events, since more pupils may watch, say, football rather than basketball.

NUMBER LINE

✥ *directed numbers, inequalities, inequations*

NUMBER PATTERNS

There are thousands of number patterns around, and they occur in so many aspects of mathematics. Here we will look at how to recognise some of them and how to display them.

Simple patterns

Look at the *differences*. These will often give you a clue as to what the pattern is.

Example 1

1, 4, 7, 10, 13 ...

The difference is 3 each time, so the pattern will continue 13, 16, 19, 22 ....

Example 2

1, 2, 4, 7, 11, 16 ...

The differences are 1, 2, 3, 4, 5 ..., so the pattern will continue 16, 22, 29, 37 ....

Example 3

1, 4, 9, 16, 25 ...

The differences are 3, 5, 7, 9..., so the pattern will continue 25, 36, 49, 64 .... Of course, if you had spotted that the pattern was 1^2, 2^2, 3^2, 4^2, 5^2 ..., then you could probably continue the pattern quite quickly.

Line patterns

Sometimes the patterns we come across involve lines, as in the following example.

Example 4

$$
\begin{aligned}
1 \times 1 &= 1 \\
11 \times 11 &= 121 \\
111 \times 111 &= 12\,321 \\
1111 \times 1111 &= 1\,234\,321 \\
11\,111 \times 11\,111 &= 123\,454\,321
\end{aligned}
$$

Can you write down the next two rows of this pattern?

We see that the number of 1s increases by one on each side of the × sign for each new line down. We can also see that the answers start from 1 and go up and then down in units of 1. The highest digit in the answer is the same number of digits from the left or right of the answer as there are 1s to the left or right of the × sign on the left-hand side.

So the next two rows will be:

$$
\begin{aligned}
111\,111 \times 111\,111 &= 12\,345\,654\,321 \\
1\,111\,111 \times 1\,111\,111 &= 1\,234\,567\,654\,321
\end{aligned}
$$

*n*th term

We often need to find the *n*th term from a series of numbers. This is a way of ***generalising*** the pattern so that we can calculate the value of any particular term in the pattern.

If the pattern always has the same difference, then the *n*th term can be found quite easily:

- Multiply *n* by the difference: call this part (a).
- Subtract the difference from the first term: call this part (b).
- The *n*th term is given by (a) + (b).

Example 5

Find the *n*th term of 7, 11, 15, 19, 23 ....

- The difference is 4 each time; so part (a) is 4*n*.
- Subtract 4 from the first term of 7 to get 3; so part (b) is 3.
- So the *n*th term is 4*n* + 3.

Example 6

Find the *n*th term of 2, 7, 12, 17, 22, 32 ...

- The difference is 5 each time; so part (a) is 5*n*.
- Subtract 5 from the first term of 2 to get –3; so part (b) is –3.
- So the *n*th term is 5*n* –3.

Example KS3 question

Explore the following number sequence. Find its *n*th term.

$$
\begin{aligned}
1 &\rightarrow 14 \\
2 &\rightarrow 17 \\
3 &\rightarrow 20 \\
4 &\rightarrow 23 \\
&\;\;\vdots \\
n &\rightarrow ?
\end{aligned}
$$

Solution

We notice that the sequence goes up by 3 each time. So the difference is 3 each time, and part (a) of our formula for the *n*th term will be 3*n*. We can find part (b) from the first term in the sequence, i.e. (14 – 3) = 11. So the *n*th term will be 3*n* + 11.

This can easily be checked by testing some of the given terms.

✦ *generalise, sequence*

NUMBERS

There are many different types of numbers.

Prime numbers

Prime numbers are numbers that have exactly two ***factors***. These two factors are always the number itself and 1.

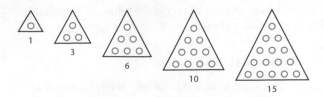

Figure N.6 Triangular numbers

The prime numbers are:

2, 3, 5, 7, 11, 13, 17, 19, 23, 29 ...

Rectangle numbers

Any whole number that is not a prime number will be a rectangle number, since it will have more than two factors (except 1 which is a special rectangle number).
The rectangle numbers are then:

1, 4, 6, 8, 9, 10, 12, 14, 15, 16, 18, 20 ...

Square numbers

A whole number multiplied by itself will give a square number. Every square number has a whole number as its **square root**.
The square numbers are:

1 , 4 , 9 , 16 , 25 , 36 , 49 , 64 ...

Triangle (or triangular) numbers

Imagine you have a lot of snooker balls. Put them into triangular patterns, as in Figure N.6, and you will see how and why the triangle numbers developed.

Notice how the *differences* of the triangle numbers increase by 1 each time, to give the list of triangle numbers as:

1, 3, 6, 10, 15, 21, 28 ...

✦ *directed numbers, number patterns, sequence, triangular numbers*

NUMERATOR

The numerator is the top number in a **vulgar fraction**. For example,

$$\frac{5}{8}$$

is a vulgar fraction. The numerator is the top number, 5. The bottom number is called the **denominator**, in this case 8.

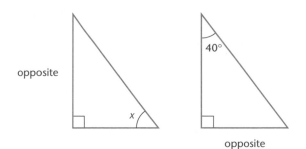

Figure O.1

OBSERVATION SHEET

✛ *data collection sheet*

OBTUSE ANGLE

An obtuse angle is larger than 90° but smaller than 180°.

OCTAGON

An octagon is an eight sided *polygon*.
   A *regular* octagon will have eight sides of equal length. Its *exterior angles* will be equal at 360°/8 = 45°. Its *interior angles* will also be equal at 180 (8–2)/8° = 135°. It will have eight *lines of symmetry* and will have *rotational symmetry* of order 8.

✛ *polygon*

OGIVE

The name given to a *cumulative frequency* curve. From the ogive you can find the *quartiles* and the *median* of the distribution.

✛ *cumulative frequency*

OPPOSITE

Opposite is the word given to that side of a right angled triangle opposite the angle that is being calculated by *trigonometry* (or that has been given, and where you are using trigonometry to calculate a side). See Figure O.1.

ORDER OF ROTATIONAL SYMMETRY

The order of *rotational symmetry* is the number of different positions which a shape can take and occupy the same space (look the same) while turning around its centre.

✛ *rotation, symmetry*

OR RULE

The **OR** rule comes from the topic of *probability*.
   To find the probability of event *A* **OR** event *B*, the probability of each event is added together. However, these two events must be *mutually exclusive*, that is to say they cannot possibly happen at the same time.

Example

In a bag that contains 5 toffees, 4 jellies and 3 mints, what is the probability of selecting one at random and it being a jelly **OR** a mint?

● The probability of selecting a jelly is 4/12.

● The probability of selecting a mint is 3/12.

● So the probability of selecting a jelly **OR** a mint is 4/12 + 3/12 = 7/12.

P

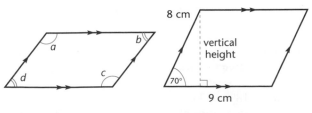

PARABOLA

This is the kind of curve you get when you draw the graph of a *quadratic* equation of the form $y = ax^2 + bx + c$. The shape is called a parabola.

↔ *quadratic*

PARALLEL

Two lines are parallel if the *perpendicular* distance between them is always the same. Lines that are parallel will usually be shown with arrows on them.
  Parallel lines do not have to be straight: train tracks are parallel, but they are not all straight. Figure P.1 gives some examples of parallel lines.

Figure P.1 Parallel lines

PARALLELOGRAM

A parallelogram has four sides and the opposite sides are of equal length, as in Figure P.2a. The opposite sides are parallel.

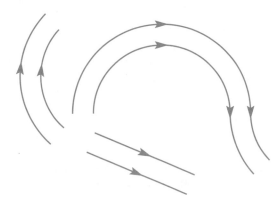

(a) Parallelogram

(b) Finding vertical height of a parallelogram

Figure P.2

● In a parallelogram any two angles *next to each other* will always add up to 180°. In Figure P.2a, for example, $a + b = b + c = c + d = d + a = 180°$.

● Also, the angles *opposite each other* will be equal. For example, $a = c$, $b = d$.

The *area* of a parallelogram is found by multiplying the base length by the vertical (perpendicular) height. The most common error in finding the area of a parallelogram is to multiply the base length by the slant height rather than the vertical height.

Example

In order to find the area of the parallelogram in Figure P.2b you need to use *trigonometry* to calculate the vertical height of the parallelogram. Then multiply this vertical height by the base length.

$$\text{vertical height} = \sin 70° \times 8 \text{ cm}$$
$$\text{area} = \sin 70° \times 8 \times 9 = 67.66 \text{ cm}^2$$
$$\text{(rounded)}$$

PASCAL'S TRIANGLE

Pascal's triangle is a particular *number pattern* that is rich in patterns. Look how each row generates the next row:

```
1st row                    1
2nd row                 1    1
3rd row              1    2    1
4th row           1    3    3    1
5th row        1    4    6    4    1
```

Try to find some of the patterns within Pascal's triangle:

● Add up each row and see what you notice. Try to find the sum of the nth row.

● Look diagonally and see what patterns you can see.

● If you ignore the 1s, which rows have evens, odds, primes, etc.?

PATTERNS

↔ *number patterns*

PENTAGON

A pentagon is a five sided *polygon* (Figure P.3).
  The sum of the *interior angles* of a pentagon is 540°.
  A *regular* pentagon has five sides of equal length. The interior angles of a regular pentagon are all 108°. The *exterior angles* of a regular pentagon are all 72°. A regular pentagon has five *lines of symmetry* and has *rotational symmetry* of order 5. It does not show *tessellation*.

↔ *polygon*

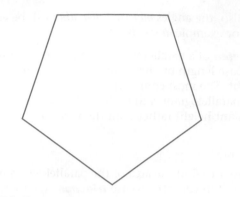

Figure P.3 Pentagon

PERCENTAGE

A percentage means 'out of a hundred'. So:

- 1% means 1 out of 100 or 1/100 or 0.01.

- 3% means 3 out of 100 or 3/100 or 0.03;
  and so on.

Changes of form

Fractions to percentages

To change any *fraction* into a percentage, all you need to do is to multiply the fraction by 100. What this is doing is finding the fraction of 100. For example,

$$\frac{5}{8} \text{ would become } \frac{5}{8} \times 100 = 62.5\%$$

Percentages to fractions

To change a percentage into a fraction, simply express the percentage as a fraction over 100 and then cancel down. For example,

$$45\% = \frac{45}{100} = \frac{9}{20} \text{ (cancelled by 5s)}$$

$$31\% = \frac{31}{100} \text{ (will not cancel)}$$

Percentages to decimals

To change a percentage to a *decimal*, simply divide the percentage by 100. This is done by moving the decimal point two places to the left. For example,

    35% becomes 0.35 as a decimal
     6% becomes 0.06 as a decimal

Decimals to percentages

To change from a decimal to a percentage, simply multiply by 100. For example,

    0.35 becomes $0.35 \times 100 = 35\%$ as a percentage

Percentage of

To calculate the percentage of something you first change the percentage to a decimal and then multiply.

Example 1

Find 8% of £135.

Calculate $0.08 \times 135 = £10.80$. So 8% of £135 is £10.80.

Percentage increase

There is a long way and a short way for doing these. Look at both ways and use whichever you feel most comfortable with.

The long way

Find the percentage and add it on.

Example 2

Increase £120 by 9%.

Calculate 9% of £120: $0.09 \times 120 = 10.8$.
The increase will be £120 + £10.80 = £130.80.

The short way

Change the percentage to a decimal and then add this to 1. Now multiply this number by the amount to be increased.

Example 3

Increase £145 by 7%.

Change 7% to 0.07, and add it to 1 to give 1.07. Then calculate $£145 \times 1.07 = £155.15$.

Percentage decrease

As for percentage increase, there is a long way and a short way for doing these.

The long way

This again means calculating the percentage, but this time *subtracting* it from the original.

Example 4

Decrease 34 kg by 18%.

Calculate 18% of 34 kg: $0.18 \times 34 = 6.12$.
The decreased amount is 34 kg – 6.12 kg = 27.88 kg.

The short way

This again requires you to change the percentage to a decimal, but then you must *subtract* this from 1 before multiplying by the original amount.

Example 5

Decrease 90 minutes by 15%.

Change 15% to 0.15: then 1 – 0.15 = 0.85. Calculate
0.85 × 90 minutes = 76.5 minutes.

PERCENTILES

These are like *quartiles*, but whereas quartiles divide the
sample into four, percentiles divide the sample into 100.
    On a *cumulative frequency* diagram you can
express the cumulative frequency as a percentage.
The percentiles are then found by going across to the
cumulative frequency curve and then down to the
value on the horizontal axis.

Example

Find the 40th percentile in Figure P.4.

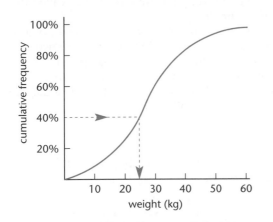

Figure P.4 Finding the 40th percentile value

To find 40% on the cumulative frequency diagram,
look horizontally along the curve and then vertically
down to read what the 40th percentile will be. In
this case it is 25 kg.

✛ *cumulative frequency*

PERIMETER

The perimeter is the total length all the way round a
flat shape.

Example 1

The *square* in Figure P.5 has a perimeter of

(2 + 2 + 2 + 2) or (4 × 2 cm) = 8 cm

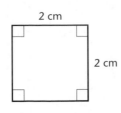

Figure P.5

Example 2

The *parallelogram* in Figure P.6 has a perimeter of

(4 + 1.5 + 4 + 1.5) or 2 × (4 cm + 1.5 cm)
= 2 × 5.5 cm = 11 cm

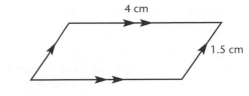

Figure P.6

Example 3

The *triangle* in Figure P.7 has a perimeter of

(2.5 + 3 + 5) = 10.5 cm

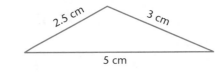

Figure P.7

Example 4

The *circle* in Figure P.8 has a perimeter (which is the
circumference) given by

circumference = π × diameter
            = π × 8 = 25.1 cm (rounded)

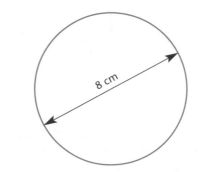

Figure P.8

PERPENDICULAR

If two lines are perpendicular then the lines are at
90° to each other (see Figure P.9a).

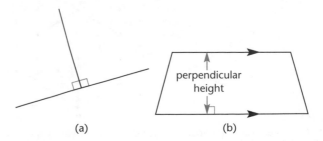

(a)   (b)

Figure P.9

A perpendicular height is the height of a line at right angles to the base (see Figure P.9b). This is sometimes called 'vertical' height, and is quite different from 'slant' height.

● The area of a *triangle* is found by multiplying the base by the perpendicular height and then dividing by two. For example, the area in Figure P.10a is

$$(5 \times 3) \div 2 = 7.5 \text{ cm}^2$$

● The area of a *parallelogram* is found by multiplying the base length by the perpendicular height. For example, the area in Figure P.10b is

$$6 \times 8 = 48 \text{ cm}^2$$

● The area of a *trapezium* is found by multiplying the average of the parallel sides by the perpendicular height. For example, the area in Figure P.10c is

$$\frac{5 + 9}{2} \times 4 = 28 \text{ cm}^2$$

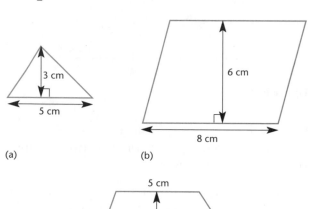

(a)   (b)

(c)

Figure P.10

When height is used in a formula it will nearly always mean perpendicular height unless stated otherwise.

PERSPECTIVE

This is the type of drawing that we do *not* do in mathematics. The drawings we do in mathematics are either *scale* drawings or **actual size** drawings.

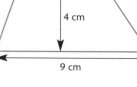

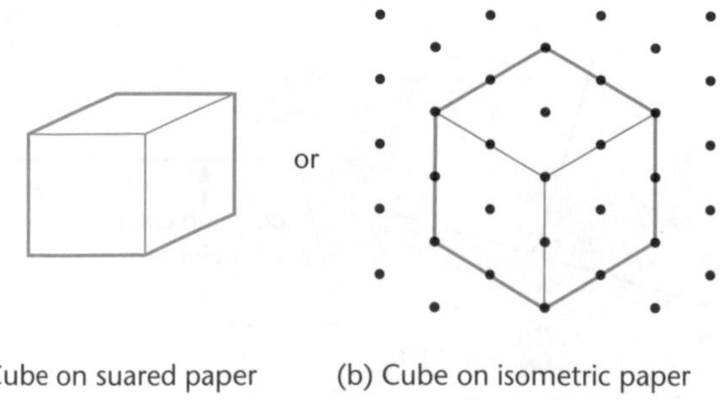

(a) Cube on suared paper   (b) Cube on isometric paper

Figure P.11

If we were to draw a cube in mathematics it would look like that shown in Figure P.11. Here the cube is drawn on squared or isometric paper.

By contrast, if the cube was to be drawn in perspective it would look like that shown in Figure P.12.

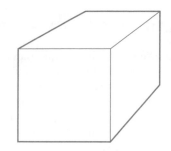

Figure P.12 Cube drawn in perspective

Can you see the difference? If you look carefully, the lines going into the distance are *not* parallel. In fact they are all heading for the same point, called the *vanishing point*.

Perspective is drawn as you would *see* an object from different positions. Mathematical drawing is done so that actual sizes can be compared. In mathematics you should avoid drawing in perspective, *unless* you are asked to draw a diagram to help you to visualise an actual situation.

Example KS3 question

Figure P.13 shows a wooden block drawn on isometric paper.

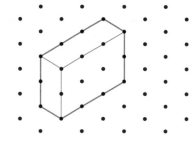

Figure P.13

It rolls by rotating about each small edge in turn, as in Figure P.14.

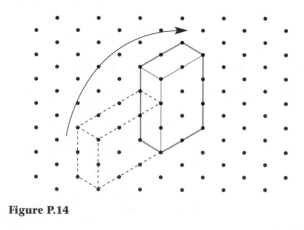

Figure P.14

Draw the faces of the block you would see after the second roll.

Solution

You will have to visualise the block rolling over and draw what you would then actually see, as in Figure P.15.

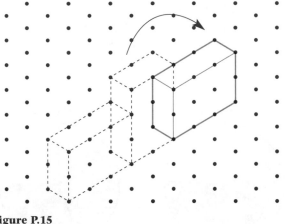

Figure P.15

You could draw in the previous blocks in dashed lines to give you the positions before the second roll. However, the *new* block has all its seen sides shown as solid with no hidden lines drawn in. Note that because the question did not put in any hidden lines, neither do we.

Pi

Pi is a constant number, even though it is impossible to write down an exact value for that number. It is the number equal to the ratio between the circumference of a circle and its diameter. Its actual value is approximated to 3.142 for calculations, although it is much more accurate to use the value on your calculator. (Look for the key labelled π.) Pi is written as the Greek letter π.

Pi is used in the following calculations:

circumference of circle	$= \pi \times \text{diameter}$
area of circle	$= \pi \times (\text{radius})^2$
volume of cylinder	$= \pi \times (\text{radius})^2 \times \text{height}$

After your calculations involving π your calculator will always give you a lot of decimal places, so care is needed to round off suitably. As a general rule always round off to one more *significant figure* than the information given.

PICTOGRAM

A pictogram is a way of illustrating data. It is like a *bar chart* but the 'bars' are made up of shapes and not bars.

Example

A survey asked 100 people what was their favourite flower. The results are illustrated in the pictogram in Figure P.16.

roses	✸	✸	✸	✸
tulips	✸	﹚		
daffodils	✸	✸	⌐	
pansies	✸	✸	﹚	
other	✸	✸		

Key
✸ represents 10 people
﹚ represents 5 people
⌐ represents 2 people

Figure P.16 Pictogram

Note that a pictogram will always need a **key**. This key may be drawn to represent different numbers of units. For example, here half the flower represents half of 10 people which is 5 people. The problem with a pictogram, however, is how to represent even smaller parts; here the stalk of the flower represents 2 people.

Example KS3 question

The pictogram in Figure P.17 shows the number of animals in a zoo. Each whole animal in the pictogram stands for 4 animals in the zoo.

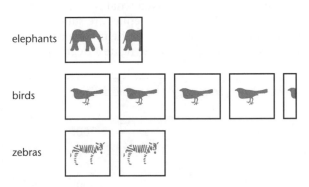

Figure P.17

(a) How many (i) elephants (ii) zebras in the zoo?

(b) Tina looked at the pictogram. She thought there were 18 birds in the zoo. Explain why Tina is wrong.

(c) There are also 7 lions in the zoo. Draw what would be on the pictogram to illustrate the 7 lions.

Solution

(a) Use the key that each whole animal picture represents 4 animals; then half an animal picture represents 2 animals.

   (i)   There are 4 + 2 = 6 elephants.

   (ii) There are 4 + 4 = 8 zebras.

(b) You need to explain that Tina thought the little bit of bird represented half the block to give 2. In fact it looks as though it is only a quarter of the block, and so represents 1 bird. There are 17 birds in the zoo.

(c) You need to draw a block with a complete lion in it, and then three-quarters of a block with three-quarters of a lion in it (Figure P.18).

Figure P.18

PIE CHART

A pie chart is a neat way to illustrate data. It is a circle divided into different sized sectors, each representing a different item of data.

Constructing a pie chart

From a frequency table you have to find the fraction of total frequency represented by each item and then multiply that fraction by 360°. Look at the following example to see how this is worked out.

Example

A group of people were asked what their favourite night-time drink was. Their replies are summarised below in the following table. (The calculated angles have been rounded off to the nearest degree.)

Item	Frequency	Calculation	Angle
Tea	34	$\frac{34}{235} \times 360°$	52°
Coffee	18	$\frac{18}{235} \times 360°$	28°
Cocoa	86	$\frac{86}{235} \times 360°$	132°
Warm milk	21	$\frac{21}{235} \times 360°$	32°
Ovaltine	51	$\frac{51}{235} \times 360°$	78°
Others	25	$\frac{25}{235} \times 360°$	38°
Totals	235		360°

See how we use the *total frequency* to calculate the angle in each sector.

When it comes to drawing the pie chart you should always draw the smallest angle first, then the next smallest, and continue in that way until you finish with the biggest angle. This is because you are quite likely to be a couple of degrees out by the time you get to your last angle, and in that case if the angle is a large one the small error would make little

difference. But it could make a difference if the error at the end involved a small angle.

Note that the total of the angles in the table should be 360° but there will be times when it actually comes to 359° or 361° because of your rounding off.

Example KS3 question

The pie charts in Figure P.19 show information from a survey of people's ages. In the survey 600 people in Sheffield and 900 people in Nottingham were asked their age.

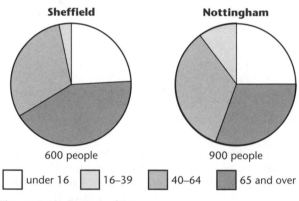

Sheffield **Nottingham**

600 people   900 people

□ under 16   ▨ 16–39   ▨ 40–64   ▨ 65 and over

Figure P.19 Survey of ages

(a) About what percentage of people in Sheffield were under 16?

(b) Of the 600 people in the Sheffield survey, approximately how many were under 16?

(c) You are asked, 'How many people in the Nottingham survey were under 16?' You reply, 'The charts show that the number is about the same as in Sheffield.' Explain why this is not right.

Solution

(a) Looking at the pie chart for Sheffield, you can see that the 'under 16' age group is almost a quarter of the circle. So this will represent around 25% of the survey. Hence we can estimate that 25% of the population of Sheffield is under 16.

(b) This is a straightforward percentage problem: find 25% of 600. This is 0.25 × 600 = 150 people.

(c) It is not right because there are more people in the Nottingham survey. So although the proportion of under 16s is about the same, the actual number involved will be higher. In fact it will be about a quarter of the 900 which is about 225.

PLANE

A plane in mathematics is a large flat surface. It is infinite in size, although we only use a small part of any plane.

Plane shapes

These are flat shapes like *triangles* and *polygons*.

PLANS

A plan of a three dimensional shape is the view you get from directly above it.

Example 1

The plan of the cube in Figure P.20a will look like Figure P.20b.

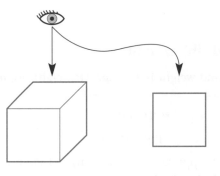

| (a) Cube | (b) Plan of cube |

Figure P.20

Example 2

The plan of the square based pyramid in Figure P.21a will look like Figure P.21b.

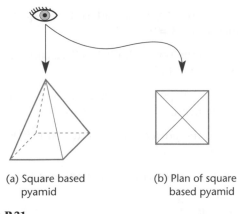

| (a) Square based pyamid | (b) Plan of square based pyamid |

Figure P.21

POINT SYMMETRY

This is another word for *rotational symmetry*. A shape has point symmetry if it can be rotated about a point so that it occupies exactly the same position in more than one place.

For example, the equilateral triangle in Figure P.22 has point symmetry as it will rotate about its centre and look the same. There are three different positions for the equilateral triangle to occupy in which it looks identical. It therefore has point symmetry of order 3.

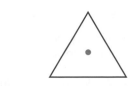

Figure P.22 Equilateral triangle

✥ *order of rotational symmetry, rotation, symmetry*

POLYGON

A polygon is a *plane* figure that has many straight sides. The names of polygons you ought to know are as follows:

triangle	3 sides
quadrilateral	4 sides
pentagon	5 sides
hexagon	6 sides
heptagon/septagon	7 sides
octagon	8 sides
nonagon	9 sides
decagon	10 sides

Polygons have two important angles: *interior angles* and *exterior angles* (Figure P.23).

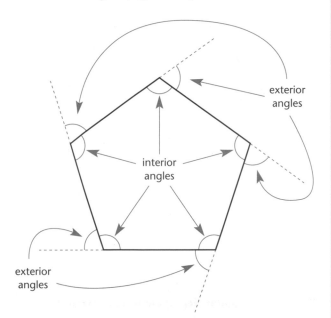

Figure P.23 Interior and exterior angles of a polygon

There are rules to help you calculate the sum of these angles in any polygon:

- The sum of *all* the exterior angles of any polygon is 360°.

- The sum of *all* the interior angles of an N sided polygon is $180(N - 2)°$.

For example, for an *octagon* the sum of the exterior angles is 360°, and the sum of the interior angles is $180 \times 6 = 1080°$.

Regular polygons

These are polygons with every side the same length and all the exterior and interior angles the same.

You can calculate the sizes of the exterior and interior angles of any *N* sided polygon with the following rules:

- The exterior angle is 360 ÷ *N*.
- The interior angle is 180° minus the exterior angle.

For example, in a regular *nonagon* (9 sides):

- The exterior angle will be 360° ÷ 9 = 40°.
- The interior angle will be 180° − 40° = 140°.

A regular polygon with *N* sides will have *N* **lines of symmetry** and will have **rotational symmetry** of order *N*. Angles at the centre of a regular polygon with *N* sides will be found by dividing 360° by *N*.

For example, in a regular *heptagon* (Figure P.24) there are seven lines of symmetry as shown. The heptagon also has rotational symmetry of order 7. Each angle at the centre will be 360° ÷ 7 = 51.4° (rounded).

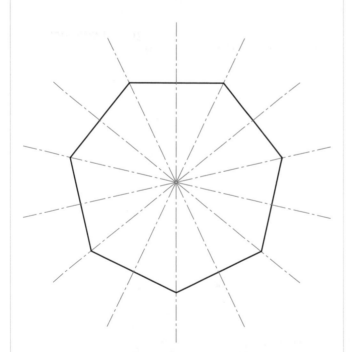

Figure P.24 Regular heptagon: lines of symmetry

✦ *symmetry*

POLYHEDRON

This is a solid three dimensional figure, whose outer faces are all plane *polygons*. Examples are a *cube* and a *tetrahedron*.

A polyhedron can be thought of as a three dimensional polygon!

✦ *cube, tetrahedron*

POSITIVE NUMBERS

✦ *directed numbers*

POUND

There are two different pounds: pound (£) money, and pound (lb) weight.

Pound (£) money

- £1 is equivalent to 100 pence.
- 1% of £1 is 1p.

Pound (lb) weight

The pound weight is an *imperial* weight not much used today.

- 1 lb is equal to 16 ounces.
- 14 lb are equal to 1 stone.
- 1 lb is approximately equal to 454 grams.
- 2.2 lb are approximately equal to 1 kilogram.

POWER

A power is the little number often put at the top right hand side of another number or letter. For example:

- 3^2 is 3 to the power 2, read as 'three squared', which is $3 \times 3 = 9$.
- 5^3 is 5 to the power 3, read as 'five cubed', which is $5 \times 5 \times 5 = 125$.
- 2^4 is 2 to the power 4, read as 'two to the power four', which is $2 \times 2 \times 2 \times 2 = 16$.
- t^3 is *t* to the power 3, read as 'tee cubed', which is $t \times t \times t$.

Other words for power are *exponent* and *index*.

✦ *exponent, index*

PRIME

Prime numbers

A prime number is a number that has exactly two *factors*.

The first few prime numbers are:

2, 3, 5, 7, 11, 13, 17, 19, 23, 29, 31, 37, 41, 43, 47, 53, 59 ...

You will see that each prime number has only two factors, itself and one. There is only one *even* prime number, namely 2.

Apart from 1, you can make every other whole number by adding two or more prime numbers together.

Prime factors

The prime factors of a number are the prime numbers that multiply together to give that number. For example:

- The prime factors of 6 are 2×3.

- The prime factors of 12 are $2 \times 2 \times 3$, written as $2^2 \times 3$.

- The prime factors of 90 are $2 \times 3 \times 3 \times 5$, written as $2 \times 3^2 \times 5$.

You find these prime factors by:

- seeing how many 2s divide into the number

- then seeing how many 3s divide into what's left

- then seeing how many 5s divide into what's left

- and so on until you end up with a prime number.

Example

Find the prime factors of 504.

```
504 ÷ 2 = 252
252 ÷ 2 = 126
126 ÷ 2 =  63   (this is an odd number, so I've
                 finished with 2)
 63 ÷ 3 =  21
 21 ÷ 3 =   7   (this is a prime number,
                 so stop)
```

So the prime factors of 504 are $2 \times 2 \times 2 \times 3 \times 3 \times 7 = 2^3 \times 3^2 \times 7$.

⟡ *factors, numbers*

PRISM

A prism is a three dimensional shape with a regular cross-section through its height or its length. The cross-section is what you get if you slice through the shape.

All the shapes in Figure P.25 are prisms, since they are shapes you could slice in such a way that each cross-section would be identical.

The volume of a prism is found by the following formula:

> volume of a prism = area of regular cross-section × length of prism

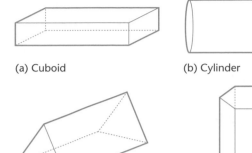

(a) Cuboid (b) Cylinder

(c) Triangular prism (d) Hexagonal prism

Figure P.25

Example

Find the volume of the prism shown in Figure P.26.

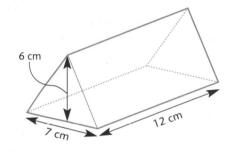

Figure P.26

The regular cross-section is a triangle. So:

$$\text{area of triangle} = \frac{1}{2} \times 6 \times 7 = 21 \text{ cm}^2$$

$$\text{volume of prism} = 21 \times 12 = 252 \text{ cm}^3$$

Example KS3 question

Work out the volume of the prism in Figure P.27. Show your working.

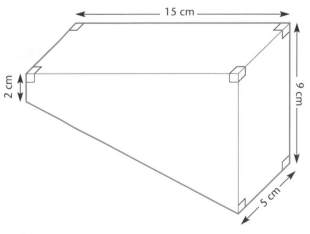

Figure P.27

Solution

The prism has a regular cross-section that is a *trapezium*. So:

$$\text{area of trapezium} = \frac{2+9}{2} \times 15 = 82.5 \text{ cm}^2$$

$$\text{volume of prism} = 82.5 \text{ cm}^2 \times 5 \text{ cm} = 412.5 \text{ cm}^3$$

PROBABILITY

In the seventeenth century, gambling fever was running high and gamblers wanted to find methods of working out their chances of winning. This led to the theory of probability. Since then we have been fascinated by probability and the prediction of results. Probability then is all about chance and predicting how many particular events are likely to happen.

Probability should be expressed as a fraction. This can be a *vulgar fraction*, a *decimal* fraction or a *percentage*. A simple probability is best expressed as a vulgar fraction. However, when you come to calculate with probabilities then a decimal fraction may be the best. Even so, many media now express probabilities as a percentage: for example, the weather forecasts often use percentage chances of rain or snow. The difficulty with a percentage is that you must change it to a decimal if you are to do any calculations with it.

In fraction or decimal form, probability always lies between 0 and 1, inclusive.

The **probability line** in Figure P.28 is useful. It shows how you could describe a chance if you knew the probability.

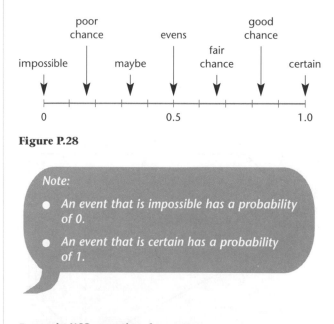

Figure P.28

> **Note:**
>
> ● *An event that is impossible has a probability of 0.*
>
> ● *An event that is certain has a probability of 1.*

Example KS3 question 1

In a bag there are 10 coloured balls: 4 are blue, 5 are white and 1 is red. You choose a ball at random out of the bag. The arrow in Figure P.29 shows the probability of the ball being red.

Figure P.29

Put an arrow on the diagram to show the probability of

(a) Choosing a white ball; label this arrow W.

(b) Choosing a blue ball; label this arrow B.

(c) Choosing a ball that is *not* red; label this arrow X.

Solution

(a) The chance of a white ball is 5/10 or 0.5. Find the position half-way along the line and put the arrow W there (Figure P.30).

(b) The chance of a blue ball is 4/10 or 0.4, just below the 0.5 mark. In fact, the arrow B should be the same distance below 0.5 as the red arrow is away from 0.

(c) This chance is 9/10 or 0.9 very close to 1. In fact, the arrow X should be as far away from 1 as the red arrow is from 0.

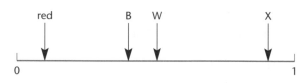

Figure P.30

You do need to be as accurate as possible, but in an exam you will still get your marks if you are close to where the arrows should be.

Experimental probability

This can be found by performing an experiment many times or making an observation many times, and keeping an accurate record of the result. The experimental probability of a particular event happening can then be worked out as:

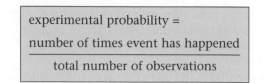

Example 1

A normal dice was rolled 100 times and the number 3 was actually obtained a total of 18 times. Give the experimental probability of obtaining the number 3.

The experimental probability is given by

$$\frac{18}{100} = \frac{9}{50} = 0.18$$

Example KS3 question 2

Kirsty does an experiment to find the probability that a drawing-pin will land on its top, as in Figure P.31.

Figure P.31 Drawing pin

She throws the drawing-pin up in the air 500 times and records the number of times it lands on its top. The following are the results she gets at each stage in the experiment:

Number of times landing on top	Throws so far	Estimate of probability
4	10	0.4
36	100	0.36
73	200	0.365
104	300	0.3467
132	400	0.33
166	500	0.332

(a) Use these results to give the best estimate of the probability that a drawing-pin will land on its top.

(b) (i) Neil dropped 800 drawing-pins onto the floor. How many would you expect to land on their top?

(ii) If Neil counted how many of his pins had landed on their top, then would you say Neil or Kirsty could estimate the probability more accurately? Explain why.

Solution

(a) The best estimate is the one you make after you have done the most experiments. So the best estimate will be the last one, 0.332.

(b) (i) The estimate is:

expected value = probability × number of trials

$$= 0.332 \times 800 = 265.6$$

A good estimate would be to say 266 (round it off).

(ii) Neil would be expected to get the better estimate because he had more trials (800 for Neil compared with 500 for Kirsty).

> *Remember: the more trials you do, the more reliable is your estimate.*

Theoretical probability

This is found by considering equally likely events. Equally likely events are those that all have an equal chance of happening. Some examples of equally likely events are:

- rolling a dice and getting 1, 2, 3, 4, 5 or 6.
- cutting a pack of cards and getting any particular card
- tossing a coin and getting a head or a tail.

Examples of events that are *not* equally likely are:

- rolling two dice and getting the totals 2, 3, 4, 5, 6, 7, etc.
- the result of a particular football match being a home win, a draw, an away win
- weather in July being snowy, rainy or sunny.

The theoretical probability of an event is found as follows:

> theoretical probability =
>
> $$\frac{\text{number of ways event can happen}}{\substack{\text{number of different equally likely events} \\ \text{that can occur}}}$$

Some examples of theoretical probabilities are as follows:

- rolling a dice and getting a 5: 1/6
- tossing a coin and getting a tail: 1/2
- cutting a pack of cards and getting a king: 4/52 = 1/13
- from a bag containing 3 red counters and 4 blue counters, choosing a blue counter: 4/7.

Example KS3 question 3

There are different ways of estimating probabilities. Three methods are:

1 Survey or experiment to collect data.

2 Looking back at old data.

3 Using equally likely outcomes.

Look at the following situations. Say whether you would use method 1, 2 or 3 to estimate the probability.

(a) The probability that a CD will last longer than an hour.

(b) The probability that a house in Birmingham will be broken into tonight.

(c) The probability that the next person you meet in the street will be colour blind.

(d) The probability that the coldest day in Britain next year will be in February.

(e) The chance of throwing a double six next go.

Solution

(a) You are going to have to collect some data: method 1.

(b) You could look at the data already on file: method 2.

(c) You will either use some old data that has already been collected or conduct your own survey: could be method 1 or 2.

(d) You could look at the old data: method 2.

(e) Yes, we can predict this one as being 1/36: method 3.

Expectation

The *expectation* of an event happening is found by multiplying the probability of the event by how many times the event has the opportunity of happening.

Example 2

I roll a dice 200 times. How many times would I expect to get the number 4?

The expectation will be

$$200 \times \frac{1}{6} = 33 \text{ (rounded)}$$

Example 3

I cut a pack of cards 500 times. How many times would I expect to get an ace?

The expectation will be

$$500 \times \frac{4}{52} = 38 \text{ (rounded)}$$

Probability of not happening

The probability of an event *not* happening is found by subtracting from 1 the probability of it happening. For example:

● The probability of rolling a dice and *not* getting a five is 1 – 1/6 = 5/6.

● If the probability of snow in March is 0.15, then the probability of *no* snow in March will be 1 – 0.15 = 0.85.

Example KS3 question 4

The Steelers and the Barons are two hockey teams. They have played each other 20 times over the past three years. The Steelers have won 60% of these matches. The Barons have won 25% of these matches.

(a) What is the probability that the next match they play will be a draw?

(b) What is the probability that the next match they play will not be a draw?

Solution

(a) From the information given, the rest of the matches would have been draws. So we work out the missing percentage as 100 – (60 + 25) = 15%. So 15% of the matches have been drawn. Change this to a decimal fraction for your answer, which will be 0.15.

(b) The chance that it is not a draw will be 1 – 0.15 = 0.85.

Mutually exclusive events

If two events *cannot* happen at the same time, then we say they are mutually exclusive. Examples of *mutually exclusive* events are:

● tossing a coin and getting a head and a tail (cannot happen at the same time with one coin).

● rolling a dice and getting a 5 and a 3 (cannot happen at the same time with one dice).

The OR rule

If two events, *A* and *B*, are mutually exclusive, then we can state the following:

> For mutually exclusive events:
>
> probability of event A OR B happening = probability of A + probability of B

Example 4

Four people have a race:

● The probability of Paul winning is 0.3.

● The probability of Amitt winning is 0.28.

● The probability of Michael winning is 0.17.

● The probability of David winning is 0.25.

What is the probability of Paul **OR** Michael winning?

The events are mutually exclusive so we add their probabilities. The probability of Paul **OR** Michael winning is 0.3 + 0.17 = 0.47.

Independent events

If two events *can* happen at the same time, then we say that they are *independent*. Examples of independent events are:

● rolling two dice and getting a 5 and then a 6

● being dealt two cards, an ace and then a king.

The AND rule

If we have two (or more) independent events, *A* **AND** *B*, we can state the following:

> For independent events:
>
> probability of event A and B happening =
> probability of A × probability of B

Example 5

What is the probability of rolling a dice twice **AND** getting a 1 and then a 2?

$$\text{probability} = \frac{1}{6} \times \frac{1}{6} = \frac{1}{36} = 0.028 \text{ (rounded)}$$

Example 6

The probability of Ritu getting her homework all correct is 0.85. The probability of Sally getting her homework all correct is 0.35. What is the probability of them *both* getting the homework right?

'Both' implies the **AND** rule, which means *multiply* the probabilities:

$$\text{probability} = 0.85 \times 0.35 = 0.2975$$

Tree diagrams

A *tree diagram* can help us to see all the possibilities in a given situation, and usually makes use of the **OR** rule and the **AND** rule in the same situation.

Follow through the next example, which uses a tree diagram.

Example 7

Two cards are dealt out. What is the probability of

(a) both being aces

(b) one being an ace

(c) at least one being an ace?

The tree diagram is drawn as in Figure P.32 with the probabilities being put on the branches. Note that the second set of probabilities depend on which card has been chosen as the first card.

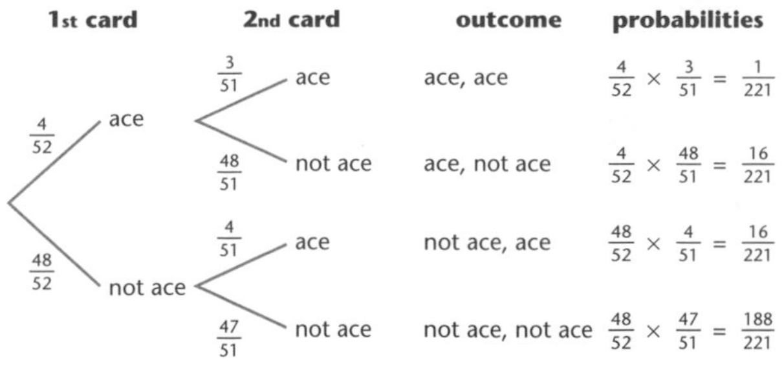

Figure P.32 Tree diagram and probability calculations

The probabilities of the combined events have been calculated using the **AND** rule:

(a) The probability of both being aces is shown on the tree diagram as

$$\frac{1}{221} = 0.0045 \text{ (rounded)}$$

(b) The probability of one ace can be seen on the tree diagram as having two possibilities:

ace, then no ace: probability $= \frac{16}{221}$

no ace, then ace: probability $= \frac{16}{221}$

So the probability of one **OR** the other happening is found by *adding* their probabilities:

$$\frac{16}{221} + \frac{16}{221} = \frac{32}{221} = 0.145 \text{ (rounded)}$$

(c) The probability of at least one being an ace can be found in two different ways.

(i) Find the probability of obtaining either one ace **OR** two aces. To do this, *add* their probabilities:

$$\frac{32}{221} + \frac{1}{221} = \frac{33}{221} = 0.149$$

(ii) Find the probability of *not* getting any aces at all. To do this, subtract the probability of no ace **AND** no ace from 1:

$$1 - \frac{188}{221} = \frac{33}{221} = 0.149$$

It is useful to see both these methods, since in different problems one method may be much better to use than the other.

PRODUCT

The product of two numbers is the answer you get when you multiply them together. For example:

● The product of 3 and 7 is 21 since $3 \times 7 = 21$.

● The product of –2 and 3 is –6 since $-2 \times 3 = -6$.

✦ *multiply*

PROPORTION

There are two types of proportion you may meet, *direct* and *inverse*.

Direct proportion

If A is directly proportional to B then there is a multiplier K such that $A = K \times B$ (K is called the **constant of proportionality**).

Work through the following example to see how problems involving direct proportion are sorted out.

Example 1

The cost of hiring a hall is directly proportional to the number of people there. When there were 110 people there, the hire charge was £715. How much will the hire charge be for 75 people?

Since cost is directly proportional to people,

cost = $K \times$ people

When there are 110 people the cost is £715. Hence

$715 = K \times 110$

$\dfrac{715}{110} = K = 6.5$

So

cost = £6.50 $\times$ people

So if there are 75 people,

cost = £6.50 $\times$ 75 = £487.50

Inverse proportion

If A is inversely proportional to B then A multiplied by B will always be the same number. This is often written as:

$A = \dfrac{K}{B}$ or $A \times B = K$

Follow through the following example.

Example 2

The time taken for a journey is inversely proportional to the speed of a vehicle. When the speed is 50 km/h the time taken is 35 minutes. How long will the journey take at a speed of 45 km/h?

Since time is inversely proportional to speed,

time = $\dfrac{K}{\text{speed}}$ and time $\times$ speed = K

The time is 35 when the speed is 50, so

$35 \times 50 = K = 1750$

This means that

time = $\dfrac{1750}{\text{speed}}$

So when the speed is 45, the time will be

$\dfrac{1750}{45}$ = 38.9 minutes (rounded)

Other difficulties

Often the proportion situations you have to deal with also involve *squares*, *cubes* and *square roots*. You simply treat them as above, but take particular care with the squaring, cubing or square rooting.

Example 3

The volume of a sphere is directly proportional to the cube of the radius. The volume of a sphere of radius 4 cm is 268 cm³. Find the volume of a sphere of radius 5 cm.

Since volume is directly proportional to (radius)³,

volume = $K \times$ (radius)³

The volume is 268 cm³ and the radius is 4 cm. So

$268 = K \times 4^3 = K \times 64$

Hence

$K = \dfrac{268}{64} = 4.1875$ (do not round off)

So

volume = 4.1875 $\times$ (radius)³

When the radius is 5 cm,

volume = 4.1875 $\times$ 5³ = 4.1875 $\times$ 125 = 523 cm³
(rounded)

PROTRACTOR

✛ *angles*

PYRAMID

A pyramid is a three dimensional shape that has a plane base and a top (vertex) which is a single point.

It is usual for the base of a pyramid to be a *polygon* or a *circle* as in Figure P.33.

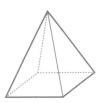 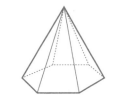

(a) Square based pyramid   (b) Hexagonal based pyramid

(c) Cone

Figure P.33

The volume of a pyramid is found by the following formula:

$$\text{volume of a pyramid} = \frac{\text{base area} \times \text{height}}{3}$$

A right pyramid

This is a pyramid that has the vertex directly above the centre of the base.

PYTHAGORAS

Pythagoras was a Greek mathematician who lived most of his life in southern Italy in the late sixth century BC. He was a philosopher as well as a mathematician. He is best known for his formula:

> *The square on the hypotenuse is equal to the sum of the squares on the other two sides in a right angled triangle.*

In terms of Figure P.34, this can be written as

$a^2 = b^2 + c^2$

This allows you to calculate the third side if you know the other two in a ***right angled triangle***.

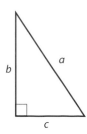

Figure P.34

Example 1

Find the ***hypotenuse*** in the triangle in Figure P.35.

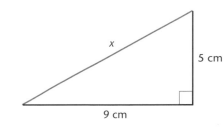

Figure P.35

Substituting the given lengths into the formula of Pythagoras, you get:

$x^2 = 5^2 + 9^2 = 25 + 81 = 106$

Hence $x = \sqrt{106} = 10.3$ cm (rounded).

Example 2

Find the missing length in the triangle in Figure P.36.

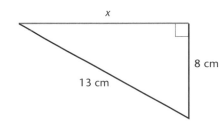

Figure P.36

Substituting the given lengths into the formula of Pythagoras, you get:

$x^2 + 8^2 = 13^2$

$x^2 + 64 = 169$

$x^2 \quad\ = 169 - 64 = 105$

$x \quad\ = \sqrt{105} = 10.2$ cm (rounded)

> *Note:*
>
> - *If you want to find the hypotenuse: you square, add, then square root.*
>
> - *If you want to find a small side: you square, subtract, then square root.*

Example KS3 question

A box has a piece of wood fixed at the back as in Figure P.37. Calculate the length of this piece of wood.

Solution

We recognise that the triangle is right angled, and we need to use the formula of Pythagoras. Apply this formula to give

$$x^2 = 110^2 + 170^2$$

(notice that I call the missing length x). This gives

$$x^2 = 12\ 100 + 28\ 900 = 41\ 000$$

$$x = \sqrt{41\ 000} = 202.5 \quad \text{(rounded)}$$

We would say the piece of wood is 202 cm long.

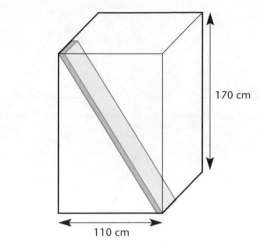

170 cm

110 cm

Figure P.37

QUADRATIC

A quadratic is an expression that involves *powers* of 2, but none higher than 2. For example,

x^2, $x^2 + 4x$, $t^2 + 5t + 4$, $x^2 + y^2$, $(x + 1)(x - 4)$

Quadratic equations

These are *equations* of the type

$x^2 = 16$

which have two answers, in this case

$x = 4$ and -4.

They are also equations of the type

$x^2 + x = 50$

which are solved by *trial and improvement*.

Quadratic graphs

A quadratic equation of the form

$y = ax^2 + bx + c$

will be a curve (a *parabola*) that looks like Figure Q.1 when the a is positive, and like Figure Q.2 when the a is negative.

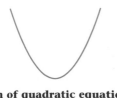

Figure Q.1 Graph of quadratic equation with a positive a

Figure Q.2 Graph of quadratic equation with a negative a

To draw a quadratic curve you do need to plot quite a few points. You should then draw a smooth curve through all the points plotted, taking great care to make sure you have a nice rounded smooth bottom to your curve (or top if a is negative).

Example
Draw the graph of $y = x^2 - 2x - 3$ for $-2 < x < 4$.

First draw up a table of values as shown:

x	-2	-1	0	1	2	3	4
x^2	4	1	0	1	4	9	16
$-2x$	4	2	0	-2	-4	-6	-8
-3	-3	-3	-3	-3	-3	-3	-3
y	5	0	-3	-4	-3	0	5

This is then plotted to give you a graph as shown in Figure Q.3.

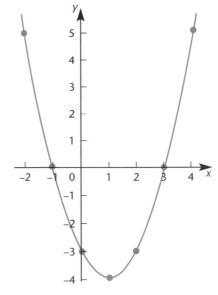

Figure Q.3

↔ *equations, expand, graphs*

QUADRILATERAL

A quadrilateral is a four sided *polygon* (Figure Q.4). Its interior angles all add up to 360°.

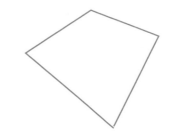

Figure Q.4 Quadrilateral

Some special quadrilaterals are shown in Figure Q.5:

- *square:* all four sides are the same length and all angles are equal to 90° (Figure Q.5a)

- *rectangle:* all the angles are 90° and the opposite sides are equal in length (Figure Q.5b)

- *rhombus:* all the sides are the same length and the diagonals cross at 90° (Figure Q.5c)

- *parallelogram:* the opposite sides are parallel and the opposite sides are of equal length (Figure Q.5d)

- *trapezium:* just one pair of opposite sides is parallel (Figure Q.5e)

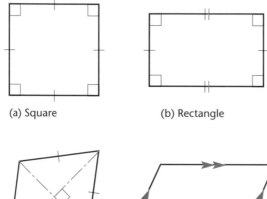

(a) Square   (b) Rectangle

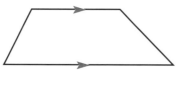

(c) Rhombus   (d) Parallelogram

(e) Trapezium

Figure Q.5

Cyclic quadrilateral

This is a quadrilateral whose vertices (corners) all touch the same circumference of a circle.

The opposite angles add up to 180°, e.g. in Figure Q.6 $a + b = 180°$ and $c + d = 180°$.

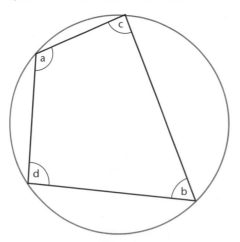

Figure Q.6 Cyclic quadrilateral

Example KS3 question

(a) What is the size of angle A in Figure Q.7?

(b) What facts about angles did you use?

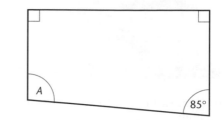

Figure Q.7

Solution

(a) We need to know that all the angles of a quadrilateral add up to 360°. So add up all the given angles and subtract this value from 360°: what you're left with is angle A. This gives

$$A = 360 - (90 + 90 + 85) = 95°$$

Alternatively, you may have recognised that the two side lines are parallel, because of the two right angles at the top. It follows that angle A and 85° are *supplementary angles*, that is, they add up to 180°: hence angle $A = 180 - 85 = 95°$.

(b) The facts will be whichever you used to obtain the answer in (a).

✦ *polygon*

QUADRILLION

This is equal to a million million million million, which is equivalent to 10^{24}.

QUARTILE

Quartiles are found by dividing a *cumulative frequency* into four equal distributions.

Lower quartile

This is the 'score' found at one-quarter of the way into the cumulative frequency. For a frequency of number N, the lower quartile is found at

$$\frac{N + 1}{4} \text{ for } \textit{small} \text{ values of } N$$

$$\frac{N}{4} \text{ for } \textit{larger} \text{ values of } N$$

There is a view that, since a cumulative frequency is only *estimating* the quartiles, you only need use $N/4$. Although this is true, it is perhaps more straightforward to use

$$\frac{N + 1}{4} \text{ when } N \text{ is } \textit{odd}$$

$$\frac{N}{4} \text{ when } N \text{ is } even$$

This makes the calculations a little easier and, since it is an approximation, it will make little difference to the final answer.

Upper quartile

This is the 'score' found at three-quarters of the way into the cumulative frequency. As for the lower quartile, it is only an approximation. So for a frequency of N you could use

$$\frac{3(N+1)}{4} \text{ when } N \text{ is } odd$$

$$\frac{3N}{4} \text{ when } N \text{ is } even$$

Inter-quartile range

This is the difference between the upper and lower quartiles.

It is a measure of spread, and is used to compare the spread or dispersion of different distributions.

Semi-inter-quartile range

This is just half of the inter-quartile range, and again is used to compare the spread or dispersion of different distributions.

All the above measures are illustrated on the cumulative graph in Figure Q.8.

inter-quartile range = upper quartile – lower quartile
= 68 – 42 = 26

The semi-inter-quartile range then is 26 ÷ 2 = 13.

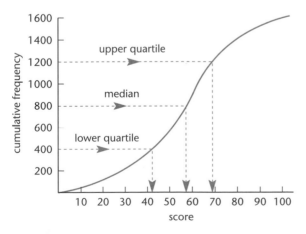

Figure Q.8

Notice that the **median** is actually the second quartile.

✛ **cumulative frequency, frequency, inter-quartile range**

QUESTIONNAIRE

A questionnaire is a **data collection sheet** with questions on it.

The questions should not be embarrassing. They should not be presented in a way that actively encourages particular answers to be given: we call such questions 'leading questions'. Some examples are as follows:

'What is your age?'

This can be an embarrassing question, so don't use it.

'Which age range are you in: 0–20, 21–40, 41–60, 61–80?'

This is a less embarrassing question to get the age range, but of course you may need more precise information for your study.

'Hanging is a cruel, evil way to treat criminals. Do you agree?'

This is a leading question: it is suggesting to people that hanging *is* cruel and evil before they give a response.

'Do you think hanging is cruel and evil?'

This is a better way of asking a question on the same subject without it being a leading question.

Every question must be such that it *can* be answered by the person answering the sheet. So, for example:

'When you go abroad, do you go to discos?'

This is a question that cannot be answered by people who do not go abroad. It would be better to give two questions such as:

'Do you go abroad?'
'If you do go abroad, do you go to discos?'

Another example is:

'How many apples do you eat a week? 1 ... 2 ... 3 ...'

This question cannot be answered by people who eat no apples or more than three. It would be better to ask:

How many apples do you eat a week? 0 ... 1 ... 2 ... 3 ... more than 3 ...'

QUOTIENT

This is the result of dividing one number or letter by another.
For example:

● The quotient of 12/4 is 3 since 12 ÷ 4 = 3.

● The quotient of x^5/x^3 is x^2.

RADIUS

A radius is the distance from the centre of a *circle* to its circumference (Figure R.1).

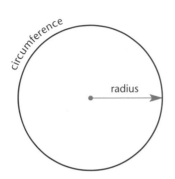

Figure R.1

The radius is connected by formula to the diameter, circumference and area of a circle:

diameter = 2 × radius

$$\text{radius} = \frac{\text{diameter}}{2}$$

circumference = 2 × π × radius

$$\text{radius} = \frac{\text{circumference}}{2 \times \pi}$$

area = π × (radius)^2

$$\text{radius} = \sqrt{\frac{\text{area}}{\pi}}$$

The value for π is best found by using the π key on your calculator.

Every circle has an **infinite number** of radii (plural of radius).

 circle

RANDOM METHOD

A method of taking a sample so that every item to be included in the sample has the same chance of being selected (from the population) as every other item.

RANGE

This is a measure in *statistics*.

It is the difference between the highest and the lowest items of data. For example,

3, 6, 8, 24, 5, 6, 2, 8, 9, 11, 10

This data has a range of (24 – 2) = 22.

The range is used to compare two different distributions of data. In other words it is a measure of spread or *dispersion*.

Inter-quartile range

The *inter-quartile range* is the difference between the upper and the lower quartile on a cumulative frequency graph. It is also a measure of spread and is used to compare two distributions.

Example KS3 question

The school netball team has an important match next week. The captain can choose Kim or Jill to be in the team. So far this season, Kim and Jill have both played in 6 matches. Their goal tally for the matches is:

Kim 11, 9, 11, 13, 11, 11
Jill   9, 1, 3, 29, 1, 23

Use the mean and the range of both girls' scores to make a choice for the next team selection. Explain your choice.

Solution

You can add up the scores and divide each girl's total by 6 to find their mean scores:

mean: Kim 11, Jill 11

You then subtract their lowest from their highest scores to find their ranges:

range: Kim 4, Jill 28

You can actually select either girl, but you must give reasons.

(a) You could choose Kim because, while their averages are the same, Kim can be relied on to score between 9 and 11 goals. In other words, she is a consistent scorer.

(b) You could choose Jill because, if she has a good day, she will score more than twice as many goals as Kim. In other words, Jill is an inconsistent scorer (higher range and therefore spread) but is capable of high scoring on occasions.

So you see, either answer can be correct. What matters is that you can illustrate how you have used the statistics.

RATE

A rate is a fixed *ratio* between two items.
When you hire a boat you are charged at a rate of, say, £2 per hour.

Two particular rates you should be familiar with are *speed* and *density*.

Speed

Speed is the rate at which you are moving, e.g. 25 miles per hour. Speed is related to distance and time in the following ways:

$$speed = \frac{distance}{time}$$

$$time = \frac{distance}{speed}$$

$$distance = speed \times time$$

Density

Density is the rate at which weight changes with volume, e.g. 20 g/cm³. Density is related to weight and volume in the following ways:

$$density = \frac{weight}{volume}$$

$$volume = \frac{weight}{density}$$

$$weight = density \times volume$$

➕ *speed, density*

RATIO

A ratio is a comparison between two quantities measured in the same *units*. For example, one part milk to two parts water is a ratio.

Often, instead of using the word 'to', we use the two dots called a colon:

milk : water = 1 : 2

↑ 'to'   ↑ 'to'

We can also write the relationship between the two quantities as a fraction:

$$\frac{milk}{water} = \frac{1}{2}$$

Example 1

We have two gear wheels as shown in Figure R.2. What is the ratio?

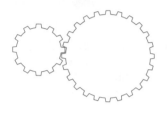

Figure R.2

The small wheel has 12 teeth and the larger wheel has 24 teeth, so that when the larger wheel has turned once, the small wheel will have turned twice. So the teeth are in the ratio

12 to 24   which is the same as   1 to 2
or   12:24   which is the same as   1:2

or $\frac{12}{24}$ which is the same as $\frac{1}{2}$

We always reduce the ratio to its simplest form, that is we cancel the numbers down by dividing both sides by the same or the top and bottom by the same. For example,

4 to 6 will cancel to 2 to 3 (divide both sides by 2)
15:50 will cancel to 3:10   (divide both sides by 5)

$\frac{12}{15}$ will cancel to $\frac{4}{5}$ (divide top and bottom by 3)

Also notice that we always have to get a ratio into the same units before we can cancel down. For example,

25 cm:40 cm = 25:40 = 5:8 (cancel cm, then divide both sides by 5)

2 m:75 cm = 200 cm:75 cm (common units first)
= 200:75   (cancel cm)
= 8:3   (divide both sides by 25)

Using a ratio to solve a problem

Example 2

Two men, Peter and Paul, agreed to invest some money in a firm in the ratio of 3:5. If the total invested is to be £42 000, how much will each man invest?

By adding the numbers in the ratio we get 3 + 5 = 8. So we see that Peter will invest 3/8 of the total and Paul will invest 5/8 of the total. So Peter invests

$$\frac{3}{8} \times £42\ 000 = £15\ 750$$

and Paul invests

$$\frac{5}{8} \times £42\ 000 = £26\ 250$$

This can be checked, as the two amounts should add up to £42 000.

Problems with ratio where one quantity is known

Example 3
A drink is made with the ingredients ginger beer, cola and lemon juice in the ratio of 5:3:1. If we have plenty of ginger beer and lemon juice but only 12 litres of cola, then how much of the other two ingredients do we need to make the drink?

By adding the numbers in the ratio we get 5 + 3 + 1 = 9. So the drink is 5/9 ginger beer, 3/9 cola and 1/9 lemon juice. If 3/9ths of the drink is the 12 litres of cola, then 1/9th will be 12/3 = 4 litres of lemon juice and 5/9ths will be 4 × 5 = 20 litres of ginger beer.

Example KS3 question
One morning in spring, Javid carried out a survey of the birds he could see. He saw 4 pigeons, 20 crows, 24 blackbirds and 48 sparrows.

(a) Write down, as simply as possible, the ratio involving how many of each type of bird he had seen.

(b) What percentage of the birds seen were crows?

Solution
(a) Write down, in the same order as the question, the numbers of each type of bird.

    pigeons : crows : blackbirds : sparrows
       4   : 20 :   24   : 48

These numbers are in the same unit (birds) and will all cancel by dividing everything by 4:

     1 : 5 :   6   : 12

(b) This is a straightforward percentage problem:

$$\frac{20}{96} \times 100 = 21\% \text{ (rounded)}$$

The 96 is the total number of birds seen.

RECIPROCAL

● The reciprocal of *N* is 1/*N*. For example, the reciprocal of 3 is 1/3, and the reciprocal of 5 is 1/5.

● The reciprocal of *A/B* is *B/A*. For example, the reciprocal of 2/3 is 3/2, and the reciprocal of 5/8 is 8/5.

You may have a reciprocal key on your calculator: it looks like $\boxed{1/x}$. You may see that you have to press $\boxed{inv}$ or $\boxed{shift}$ or $\boxed{2ndf}$ to access it. So, to find the reciprocal of any number, you could just key in your number then press the reciprocal key.

Example
What is the reciprocal of 0.125?

Key into your calculator 0.125. Then press the key $\boxed{1/x}$. You should get the display 8, which is the answer.

Reciprocal graph

The graph of *y* = *A/x*, where *A* is any positive amount, will look like Figure R.3.

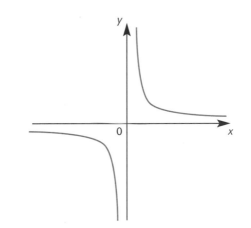

Figure R.3 Reciprocal graphs

✦ *graphs, hyperbola*

RECTANGLE

This is a four sided *polygon* with all the angles 90° and the opposite sides equal in length.

✦ *area, cuboid, length, quadrilateral, right angle*

RECTANGLE NUMBERS

These include the number 1 and any other numbers with more than two *factors*

✦ *numbers*

RECURRING

A recurring *decimal* is one that has decimal places carrying on for ever in a set pattern. For example

    1/3 = 0.333 333, etc.

We show the repeating pattern with dots on top and to the right. For example,

1/3 = 0.3̇ (dots show pattern starts and finishes on 3)

3/11 = 0.272 727 27, etc.

= 0.2̇7̇ (dots on 2 and 7 show start and end of pattern)

4/7 = 0.571 428 571 428 571 428, etc.

= 0.5̇71 428̇ (dots on 5 and 8 show start and end of pattern)

You will find that all the *fractions* with a *denominator* of 3, 6, 7, 9, 11, 13, etc. will have a recurring decimal equivalent. Fractions which have (or cancel down to) a denominator of 2, 4, 5, 8, 10, etc. will have *terminating* decimals.

REFLECTIONS

Reflections are what you see in a mirror.

A mathematical reflection is a drawing of an original shape on the opposite side of a mirror line as if it was the reflection in a normal mirror. This mirror line will be a *line of symmetry* for the original shape and the reflected shape (often called an *image*).

Some examples of reflections are shown in Figure R.4.

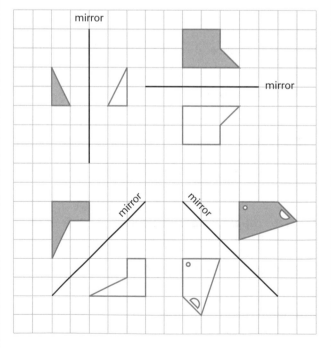

Figure R.4 Examples of reflections

Every point on the original shape is reflected in the mirror line, and a straight line from the original point to its image will be a line that is *perpendicular* to the mirror line and exactly the same distance from point to mirror as from image to mirror.

Example KS3 question

(a) Reflect each set of lines in the mirror lines shown in Figure R.5.

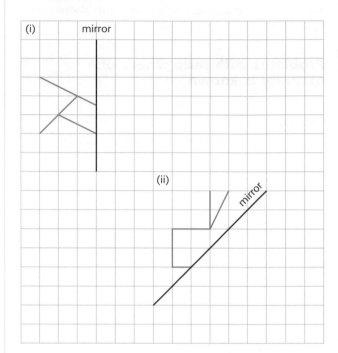

Figure R.5

(b) Now use the two mirror lines shown in Figure R.6. First reflect the set of lines in the vertical mirror line. Then reflect the whole pattern in the horizontal mirror line.

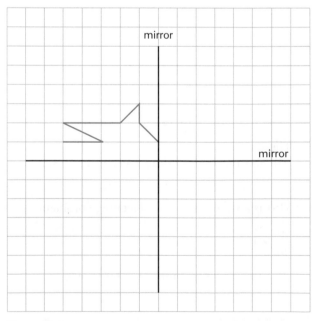

Figure R.6

Solution

(a) Always remember to imagine that the image has to be found by going straight from the object to the mirror (at right angles) and drawing the image the same distance behind as the object is in front. This will give the reflections shown in Figure R.7.

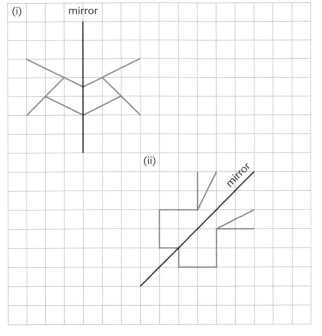

Figure R.7

(b) It didn't actually matter which you did first. As long as you worked carefully you should have ended up with the pattern in Figure R.8.

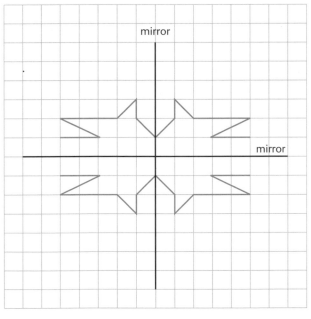

Figure R.8

-⧫- *line of symmetry, symmetry, transformation*

REFLEX ANGLE

A reflex angle is an angle bigger than 180° and smaller than 360°. It is the angle on the other side of an *acute angle* or an *obtuse angle*.

-⧫- *angles*

REGULAR

A regular polygon is one that has all its sides the same length. All the *interior angles* are the same and all the *exterior angles* are the same.

An *N* sided regular polygon will have

- exterior angles of size $360 \div N°$
- interior angles of size $180\,(N-2) \div N°$
- *N* lines of symmetry
- rotational symmetry of order *N*.

-⧫- *cross-section, polygon*

RHOMBUS

A rhombus is a special *quadrilateral*; in fact it is also a special *parallelogram* (Figure R.9).

- It has all four sides the same length.
- The opposite sides are parallel.
- The opposite angles are equal.
- Its two diagonals cross over at right angles and bisect each other.
- Each diagonal is also a *line of symmetry*.
- It has *rotational symmetry* of order 2.

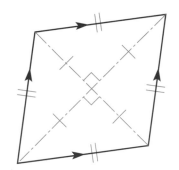

Figure R.9 Rhombus

RIGHT ANGLE

A right angle is 90°. The corners of *squares* and *rectangles* are all 90°.

A right angle is usually marked with a little square.

RIGHT ANGLED TRIANGLE

This is a triangle that has a right angle in it. The long sloping side is called the *hypotenuse* (Figure R.10).

You can use *trigonometry* and *Pythagoras'* formula in right angled triangles.

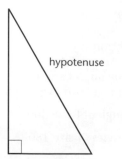

Figure R.10 Right angled triangle

RIGHT PYRAMID

This is a *pyramid* that has its vertex (top point) directly above the centre of the base.

ROOT

A root is the mathematical word for a solution of a *quadratic* equation.

Root of a number

The root of a number is generally taken to be the *square root*. So, root 9 will be 3 or –3.

The Nth root

The Nth root of a number *A* is that number which, when multiplied by itself *N* times, gives *A*.

Examples

● The square root of 25: √25 = 5 or –5, because 5 × 5 = 25.

● The cube (3rd) root of 64: $^3\sqrt{64} = 4$, because 4 × 4 × 4 = 64.

● The 4th root of 81, $^4\sqrt{81} = 3$, because 3 × 3 × 3 × 3 = 81.

You can use your calculator to find any root of any number by using the $\boxed{x^{1/y}}$ key, where *y* is the Nth root you want. You will most likely need to use the $\boxed{\text{shift}}$ or $\boxed{\text{inv}}$ or $\boxed{\text{2ndf}}$ key also. For example, if you want to find the 5th root of 7776, key in 7776 $\boxed{x^{1/y}}$ 5: this will give the result 6.

ROTATION

A rotation is a turn about some point, called the *centre* of rotation. In a mathematical rotation, every point in the shape will rotate by the same angle.

   Look at the diagrams in Figure R.11 to see examples of rotations of various shapes and through various angles.

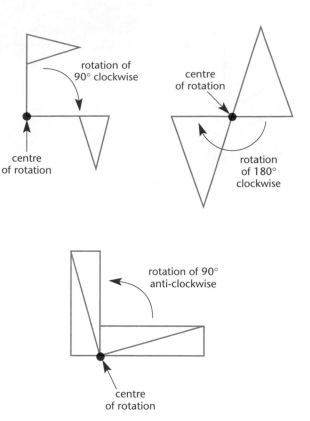

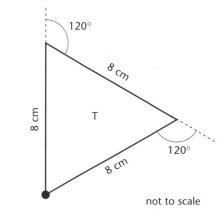

Figure R.11 Examples of rotations

Whenever you describe a rotation, you should always state the angle together with its direction (clockwise or anti-clockwise), and the centre of rotation.

Example KS3 question

(a) The shape T in Figure R.12 is an equilateral triangle of side 8 cm.

Figure R.12

The instructions to draw the shape T are as follows:

   forward 8
   turn right 120
   forward 8
   turn right 120
   forward 8

Write a set of instructions to draw an equilateral triangle that has sides 4 cm long, beginning forward from the start position.

(b) The shape P in Figure R.13 is a parallelogram.

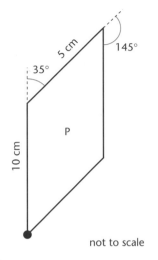

Figure R.13

Give a set of instructions to draw shape P, beginning forward from the start position.

Solution

If you have met the computer program LOGO then this is a lot easier. If you have not, then just think about breaking the instructions down one at a time in order to draw the shapes.

(a) forward 4
turn right 120
forward 4
turn right 120
forward 4

(b) forward 10
turn right 35
forward 5
turn right 145
forward 10
turn right 35
forward 5

I hope you stopped there and didn't turn back unnecessarily.

ROTATIONAL SYMMETRY

point symmetry, symmetry

ROUNDING

There are two ways of rounding off: *significant figures* or *decimal places*.

To round off to significant figures or decimal places, or even to the nearest 100, uses the same basic principle of rounding:

● Decide where you need to round off to: either a particular decimal place, or a particular significant figure, or the hundreds.

● Then look at the *next digit* to the right. If it is less than 5, you **round down** by leaving the digits as they are up to that point. If it is 5 or more than 5, you **round up** by adding 1 to the previous digit.

Look at the following examples of different roundings:

8539	rounds to 9000	to 1 significant figure
	rounds to 8500	to 2 significant figures
	rounds to 8540	to 3 significant figures

2.4615	rounds to 2.5	to 1 decimal place
	rounds to 2.46	to 2 decimal places
	rounds to 2.462	to 3 decimal places

3465	rounds to 3470	to the nearest 10
	rounds to 3500	to the nearest 100
	rounds to 3000	to the nearest 1000

The most common error is to cut off (truncate) any unwanted figures without checking to see whether the rounding off should be up or down.

Example KS3 question

Brian has labelled sticks with their lengths measured to the nearest hundredth of a centimetre, as in Figure R.14.

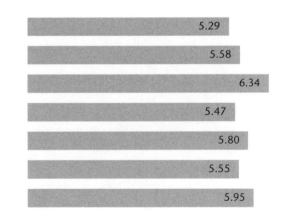

Figure R.14

He wants to put the sticks into two different boxes. In box A he puts all the sticks that are 5 cm to the nearest centimetre. In box B he puts all the sticks that are 6 cm to the nearest centimetre.

(a) Put the sticks into the correct boxes (one has been done for you in Figure R.15).

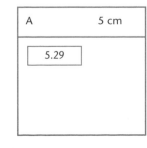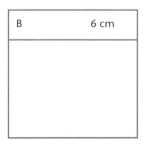

Figure R.15

(b) Brian wants to put a lot more sticks into each box.

    (i)   What is the largest possible measurement put on a stick in box A?

    (ii) What is the smallest possible measurement put on a stick in box B?

Solution

(a) Round off and put into the right box. So you should have:

       in box A: 5.29, 5.47
       in box B: 5.58, 6.34, 5.80, 5.55, 5.95

(b) (i) The largest size that will round to 5 cm will be 5.49, since the next possible number up is 5.50 which rounds up to 6. So the largest possible stick in box A is 5.49 cm.

    (ii) The smallest size that rounds to 6 cm will be 5.50 cm. So the smallest possible stick in box B is 5.50 cm.

✦ *decimal places, significant figures*

RUNNING TOTAL

✦ *cumulative frequency*

SCALE

Scale of a map

You have scales when using maps. The scale is written as a *ratio*. For example, the scale on a map could be 1:250 000. This means that 1 cm on the map represents 250 000 cm in reality, i.e. 1 cm to 2500 metres or 1 cm to 2.5 kilometres.

Scale drawings

A scale drawing is a diagram drawn to represent a bigger situation, with some scale such as 1 cm to 10 metres.

Scale factor

This is the multiplying factor of an *enlargement*. Each original length is multiplied by the scale factor to find the new length.

For example, in Figure S.1, the shape ABC has been enlarged from centre of enlargement (1, 1) with a scale factor of 2.

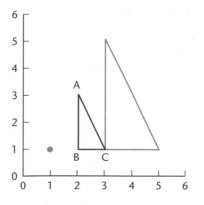

Figure S.1 Scale factor of 2

Scale of a graph

The scale on a *graph* is found on the axes and involves the labelling of the squares. In an examination the scale is nearly always given to you as it is not always easy to decide which scale might be best.

SCALE FACTOR

-+- *scale*

SCALENE

This is what we call a *triangle* that has all its sides *different* lengths.

SCATTER DIAGRAM

-+- *scatter graph*

SCATTER GRAPH

This is a *graph* that plots quite a few points which represent *two* variables. A scatter graph is used to see if there is any connection between one thing and another thing. For example:

● Do taller people have bigger feet?

● Do people with large hands weigh more?

● Do people who get good marks in Maths also get good marks in English?

● Do we sell more ice creams when it gets hotter?

● Are taller people more intelligent than smaller people?

All these situations can be tested by finding information from a lot of people and then by plotting this information as points on a scatter diagram. We can then tell if there is a connection by looking at how the points are arranged.

Correlation

The scatter graphs in Figure S.2 represent the three different types of *correlation* that can be found.

● Do taller people weigh more? Figure S.2a shows positive (or direct) correlation. It shows that the taller people are, the heavier they are likely to be.

● Is there a connection between temperature and the number of spiders seen in a house? Figure S.2b shows negative (or indirect, or inverse) correlation. It shows that the higher the temperature, the fewer spiders you get in a house.

● Is there a connection between height and maths test scores? Figure S.2c shows no correlation. It shows there is no connection between height and maths scores.

Lines of best fit

If we see there is a correlation between two things then we can draw a line of best fit, that is a line that follows the trend of the plotted *data* (Figure S.3).

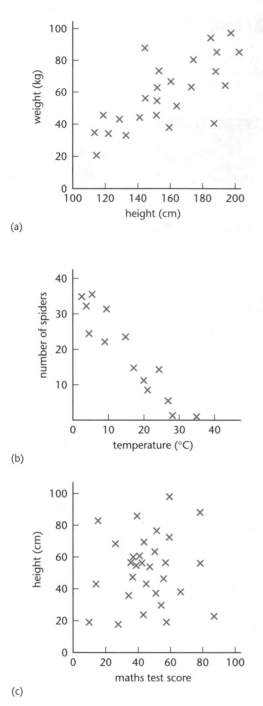

(a)

(b)

(c)

Figure S.2

When you draw a line of best fit you should be trying to:

- show the trend

- have as many points above the line as below the line

- draw the line from one side of the available graph to the other.

But beware:

- This line does *not* have to go through all the points.

- This line does *not* have to go through the origin.

- This line is *not* drawn from the first to the last point.

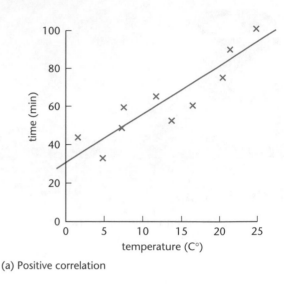

(a) Positive correlation

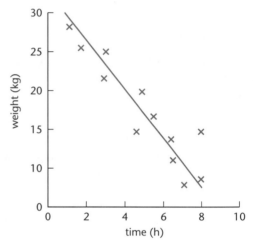

(b) Negative correlation

Figure S.3 Lines of best fit

This line is usually straight, but it could be curved. However, until you get to A-level statistics all the lines of best fit you will meet should be straight lines.

Example KS3 question

The three graphs in Figure S.4 show the sales from a shop plotted against temperature. The sales were all recorded on different Sundays during the same year. Describe what each graph shows you.

Solution

(a) Figure S.4a shows that the higher the temperature, the fewer tins of rice pudding are sold. Or, there is a negative or indirect correlation between the temperature and the number of tins of rice pudding sold.

(b) Figure S.4b shows that the temperature makes no difference to the sales of cereal. Or, there is no correlation between temperature and the sales of cereal.

(c) Figure S.4c shows that as the temperature increases, so do the sales of ice cold drink. Or, there is a positive (or direct) correlation between temperature and the number of cans of ice cold drink sold.

correlations, line of best fit

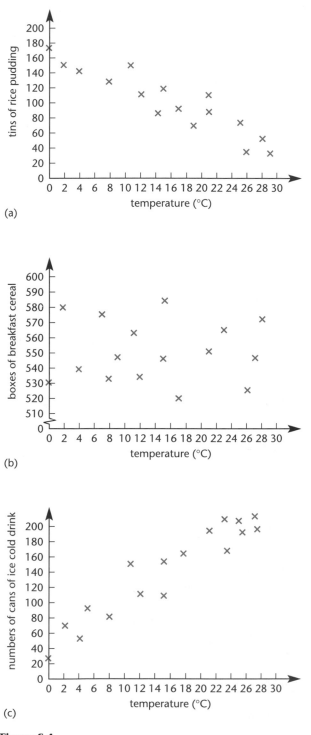

Figure S.4

SCIENTIFIC CALCULATOR

A type of *calculator* which helps you solve a wider range of problems, e.g. *trigonometry* problems. There are two types. DAL (Direct Algebraic Logic), where √36 is found by $\boxed{\sqrt{}}$. $\boxed{36}$ and 'others' where $\boxed{36}$. $\boxed{\sqrt{}}$ is used.

SEMI-INTER-QUARTILE RANGE

This is the *inter-quartile range* divided by two. It is a measure of spread used to compare two distributions.

SEPTAGON

A septagon is a *polygon* with seven sides. Its more common name is a *heptagon*.

 heptagon

SEQUENCE

A sequence is a list of *numbers* that follow some pattern. For example:

2, 4, 6, 8, 10 ...	the even numbers
1, 5, 9, 13, 17, 21 ...	starting with 1 and adding 4 each time
1, 4, 9, 16, 25, 36 ...	the square numbers
1, 1, 2, 3, 5, 8, 13 ...	the *Fibonacci* numbers

If we have a sequence we will usually need to be able to describe how the sequence runs, as in the examples above.

*n*th term

However, we will also need to be able to find the *n*th term of the sequence to help us predict any term in that sequence. We have to spot a pattern to do with $n = 1$, $n = 2$, $n = 3$, etc. Some are easy to spot, such as:

1, 2, 3, 4, 5, 6 ...	*n*th term will be n
1, 4, 9, 16, 25 ...	*n*th term will be n^2
3, 6, 9, 12, 15 ...	*n*th term will be $3n$

We need to look for clues in patterns. If the sequence increases by the same amount (difference) A each time, and starts with the number B, then the *n*th term is given by $An + (B - A)$.

Example 1

Find the *n*th term of the sequence 6, 10, 14, 18, 22, 26 ....

We see that 4 is added each time, and the sequence starts with 6. So the *n*th term is given by $4n + (6 - 4) = 4n + 2$.

Check that the 5th term is 22, from both the rule and the given sequence.

Example 2

Find the *n*th term of the sequence 1, 4, 7, 10, 13, 16 ....

We see that 3 is added each time, and the sequence starts with 1. So the *n*th term is given by $3n + (1 - 3) = 3n - 2$.

Check that the 5th term is 13, from both the rule and the given sequence.

 generalise, number patterns

SET

A set is a collection of **elements** (e.g. numbers), often denoted by the use of curly brackets. For example, {2, 4, 6, 8} is the set of positive and even *numbers* less than 10.

SIGNIFICANT FIGURES

Significant figures (s.f.) are used when we wish to approximate or round answers off. Counting the number of actual *digits* will often tell us the number of significant figures involved. For example:

8	has 1 significant figure
9.3	has 2 significant figures
47.7	has 3 significant figures
0.1845	has 4 significant figures

However, when 0s are in the number, we must know when to count them as a significant figure and when not to.

- When the 0s come at the end of the number or at the beginning of the number, then we do *not* count them as significant figures. For example:

50	has 1 significant figure
400	has 1 significant figure
56 000	has 2 significant figures
0.67	has 2 significant figures
0.009	has 1 significant figure
0.000 13	has 2 significant figures

- When the 0s come between digits, we *do* count them as significant figures. For example:

105	has 3 significant figures
2070	has 3 significant figures
5002	has 4 significant figures

Rounding off to a given number of significant figures

The rules are similar to other rounding offs:

- Look at the first digit that 'has to go'.

- If this is less than 5, then leave the digits on the left (if there are any) alone.

- If the digit is 5 or more than 5, then add 1 to the digit on the left.

- Then put 0s in to keep the place value of the original number.

For example:

832	to 1 s.f. is 800 since the 3 is less than 5
8.7621	to 2 s.f. is 8.8 since the 6 is more than 5

Look at the following table to see how these rules work for the numbers chosen:

Number	Correct to 1 s.f.	Correct to 2 s.f.	Correct to 3 s.f.
34.87	30	35	34.9
159.2	200	160	159
10 942	10 000	11 000	10 900
0.07158	0.07	0.072	0.0716

Exceptions

Do be aware that a given number, say 600, could actually be an original number rounded to 1, 2 or 3 s.f. For example:

647	rounds to 600	1 s.f.
595	rounds to 600	2 s.f.
599.7	rounds to 600	3 s.f.

However, if we were given the number 600 with no other explanation, then we would assume that the smallest number of significant figures applies, in this case 1 s.f.

decimal places, rounding

SIMILAR

Two shapes are said to be similar if one is an *enlargement* of the other. All the corresponding angles will be the same. All the corresponding lengths will be in the same ratio (1 : scale factor).

Example 1

The two triangles ABC and PQR in Figure S.5 are similar. Notice that each corresponding length in PQR is three times bigger than that in ABC. All the corresponding angles are equal.

See that

angle at A = angle at P
angle at B = angle at Q
angle at C = angle at R

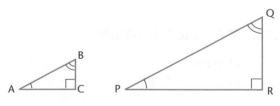

Figure S.5

Similar triangles

Problems are often set involving similar *triangles*. The solutions frequently use the fact of common ratios between corresponding sides.

For the two similar triangles ABC and XYZ in Figure S.6,

$$\frac{AB}{XY} = \frac{BC}{YZ} = \frac{AC}{XZ}$$

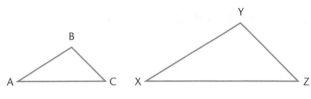

Figure S.6

Work through the following example.

Example 2

The triangles ABC and PQR in Figure S.7 are similar.

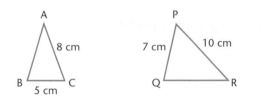

Figure S.7

Find the lengths of (a) AB and (b) QR.

(a) To find AB, we start with AB and use the ratio for which we are given both numbers:

$$\frac{AB}{PQ} = \frac{AC}{PR}$$

$$\frac{AB}{7} = \frac{8}{10}$$

$$AB = \frac{7 \times 8}{10} = 5.6 \text{ cm}$$

(b) To find QR, we start with QR and use the ratios of PR to AC for corresponding sides:

$$\frac{QR}{BC} = \frac{PR}{AC}$$

$$\frac{QR}{5} = \frac{10}{8}$$

$$QR = \frac{5 \times 10}{8} = 6.25 \text{ cm}$$

Frequent similar triangle situations

If you have to find missing lengths in problems involving similar triangles, it is a good idea to separate the two similar triangles out, put on all their measurements and then solve.

Example 3

The triangle in Figure S.8 is shown with AE parallel to BD. Find the length DE.

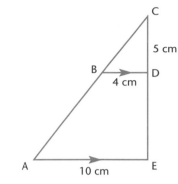

Figure S.8

Separate out the two similar triangles (Figure S.9). Let the length DE be d. Then

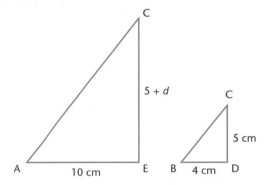

Figure S.9

$$\frac{CE}{CD} = \frac{AE}{BD}$$

$$\frac{5 + d}{5} = \frac{10}{4}$$

$$5 + d = \frac{5 \times 10}{4} = 12.5$$

$$d = 12.5 - 5 = 7.5 \text{ cm}$$

Example KS3 question

Calculate the length BE in Figure S.10 using similar triangles. Show your working.

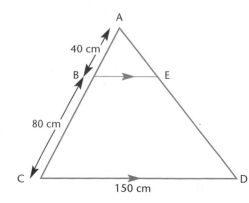

Figure S.10

105

Solution

Separate out the two similar triangles as in Figure S.11. Then by looking at corresponding sides, we can say that

$$\frac{BE}{CD} = \frac{AB}{AC}$$

$$\frac{BE}{150} = \frac{40}{120}$$

$$BE = \frac{40 \times 150}{120} = 50 \text{ cm}$$

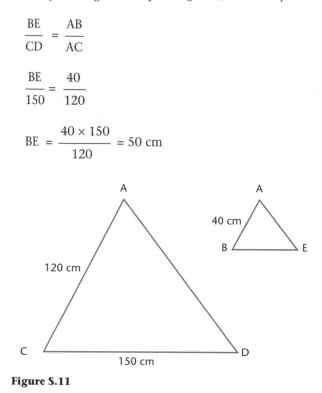

Figure S.11

SIMPLE INTEREST

Simple interest (SI) is the amount of money given as a result of leaving a sum of money in a particular account for some given time. It is based on having a principal amount P in the account for a number of years T at a rate of interest R.

There is a formula to calculate simple interest:

$$SI = \frac{PRT}{100}$$

In words:

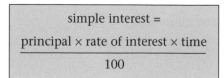

simple interest =

$$\frac{\text{principal} \times \text{rate of interest} \times \text{time}}{100}$$

Example

Joseph had £60 in an account for 3 years at 8% interest rate. The interest he earned was simple interest. How much will this interest be?

Principal is £60, time is 3 years, rate is 8% . So

$$SI = \frac{PRT}{100} = \frac{60 \times 3 \times 8}{100} = 14.4$$

So the simple interest will be £14.40.

When the amount of simple interest is added each year to the original amount it becomes **compound interest**.

✦ *compound interest*

SIMPLIFICATION

This is what we do in **algebra** to make expressions look as simple as possible. It can either be *factorising*, or *expanding* then simplifying.

Factorising

For example:

$4x + 8y$ would simplify to $4(x + 2y)$

$x^2 - 3x$ would simplify to $x(x - 3)$

Expanding and simplifying

For example:

$3(x + 5y) + 2(4x - 3y) = 3x + 15y + 8x - 6y$

$$= 11x + 9y$$

Example KS3 question

Write down an expression for the perimeters of each of the shapes in Figure S.12. Write each expression in its simplest form.

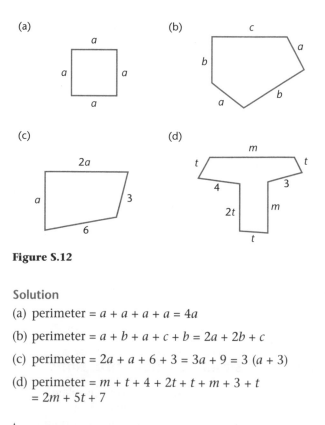

Figure S.12

Solution

(a) perimeter = $a + a + a + a = 4a$

(b) perimeter = $a + b + a + c + b = 2a + 2b + c$

(c) perimeter = $2a + a + 6 + 3 = 3a + 9 = 3(a + 3)$

(d) perimeter = $m + t + 4 + 2t + t + m + 3 + t$
    $= 2m + 5t + 7$

✦ *factorising, expand*

Simultaneous equations

Simultaneous equations can be solved either by *graph* or by *algebra*.

Graph

Example 1

Solve

$$x + y = 8$$
$$y = 2x + 3$$

You need to draw both graphs on the same pair of axes. Both are ***linear***, and so will give a straight line. We only need to find three co-ordinates that fit each equation to be sure of drawing it correctly:

x	$x + y = 8$	$y = 2x + 3$
0	(0, 8)	(0, 3)
1	(1, 7)	(1, 5)
2	(2, 6)	(2, 7)

The graphs are as in Figure S.13. The solution is found by looking at the point where the graphs cross each other. Here that point is (1.7, 6.3). So the solution is $x = 1.7$, $y = 6.3$.

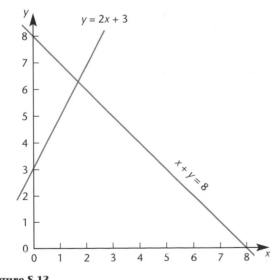

Figure S.13

⟵╬⟶ *equations, intersection*

Algebra

We will add or subtract the two equations together in order to eliminate one of the two letters (variables). But they must have the same number in front of the letter in order to be eliminated in this way.

Example 2

Solve

$$3x + 5y = 23$$
$$x + 5y = 21$$

y can be eliminated by *subtracting* these two equations since they both have $+ 5y$. This will give us

$$2x = 2$$
$$x = 1$$

Having found one solution we can substitute this into the simplest original equation to get:

$$1 + 5y = 21$$
$$5y = 21 - 1 = 20$$
$$y = \frac{20}{5} = 4$$

So the solution will be $x = 1$ and $y = 4$.

Example 3

Solve

$$2x + y = 10$$
$$5x - y = 11$$

We eliminate y by *adding* the equations:

$$7x = 21$$
$$x = \frac{21}{7} = 3$$

Having found one solution, we substitute it into the simplest original equation to get:

$$2 \times 3 + y = 10$$
$$6 + y = 10$$
$$y = 10 - 6 = 4$$

So the solution is $x = 3$ and $y = 4$.

Example KS3 question

Solve

$$x + 2y = 17$$
$$6 + x = 2y$$

Solution

The first thing is to rearrange the equations so that they look as we would expect them to look:

$$x + 2y = 17$$
$$x - 2y = -6$$

Since the y's are both $2y$, but with different signs, we can *add* the two equations to give:

$2x = 11$
$x = 5.5$

Now substitute $x = 5.5$ in $6 + x = 2y$ to give

$6 + 5.5 = 2y$
$y = 11.5 \div 2 = 5.75$

The solution then is $x = 5.5$ and $y = 5.75$.
This can be checked using the equation $x + 2y = 17$.

SINE (SIN)

Sine (abbreviated sin) is a trigonometrical ratio used to solve problems in **right angled triangles**. The definition of sine θ is

$$\sin \theta = \frac{\text{opposite}}{\text{hypotenuse}}$$

See Figure S.14.

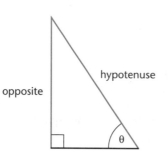

Figure S.14

Example 1
Find the length x in Figure S.15.

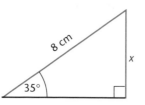

Figure S.15

From the triangle we can say

$$\sin 35° = \frac{\text{opposite}}{\text{hypotenuse}} = \frac{x}{8}$$

Then $8 \sin 35° = x$

(8 sin 35° means 8 multiplied by sin 35°.) This is done on a **scientific calculator** by one of two methods depending on the type of calculator:

DAL: type as it reads 8 | sin | 35 | =

Others: type in as 8 | × | 35 | sin | =

(notice you need the 35 before the sin)

Check that you can do this on *your* calculator to get $x = 4.59$ cm (rounded).

Example 2
Find the angle θ in Figure S.16.

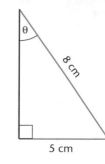

Figure S.16

From the triangle we can say that

$$\sin \theta = \frac{\text{opposite}}{\text{hypotenuse}} = \frac{5}{8}$$

So

$$\sin \theta = \frac{5}{8} = 0.625$$

We use this fact to find the size of angle θ. With 0.625 in the calculator, type into the calculator sin⁻¹ which is usually found by

shift | sin   or   inv | sin   or   2ndf | sin

Check that you can do this on your calculator to get θ = 38.7° (rounded).

SKETCH GRAPHS

A sketch graph is just what it says. It is a drawing that is not accurate but shows the type of **graph**, whether a straight line or a type of curve. We show simple points on the axes if we know them.
    The following types of sketch graph are expected at Key Stage 3:

● linear: $y = 3x - 2$

● quadratic: $y = x^2 + 1$

● reciprocal: $y = 12/x$

If you look at the material under **linear**, **quadratic** and **reciprocal** you will see examples of graphs. You need to be familiar with the type of graph associated with each type of equation in order to be able to sketch a good graph.

✛ *graphs*

SLANT HEIGHT

This is the height of a shape measured in line with the slant or slope of that shape, rather than vertically or **perpendicular**.

SOLID SHAPES

Solid shapes are three dimensional figures. The ones that you will meet are as follows.

Cube

This has each of its six faces a square (Figure S.17a). Its volume is x^3, where its side length is x.

Nets of the cube can be made (e.g. Figure S.17b).

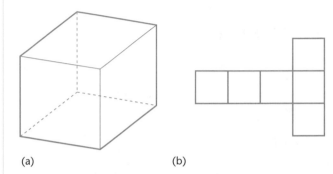

(a)   (b)

Figure S.17 Cube

Cuboid

This has opposite faces which are equal rectangles (Figure S.18a). Its volume is length × breadth × height.

Nets of the cuboid can be made (e.g. Figure S.18b).

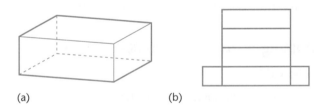

(a)   (b)

Figure S.18 Cuboid

Cylinder

This has circular ends and a regular circular cross-section (Figure S.19). Its volume is $\pi r^2 h$, where r is the radius and h the height.

You cannot have a net for a cylinder.

Figure S.19 Cylinder

Pyramid

This has a base, and sides which rise from the base to a point (vertex) (Figure S.20a). Its volume is

base area × height
_____
        3

Nets of a square based pyramid can be made (e.g. Figure S.20b).

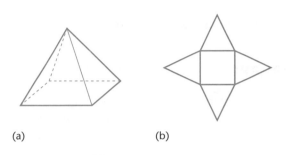

(a)   (b)

Figure S.20 Pyramid

⊹ *cube, cuboid, cylinder, net, pyramid*

Words connected with solids

● Face: the flat surface of solid shapes.

● Edge: a line where two faces meet.

● Vertex: a point where two (or more) edges meet.

⊹ *edge, face, vertex*

SOLVE

You will usually come across the word 'solve' in connection with *equations*.

● To solve an equation such as $4x - 3 = 7$ is to find the value of x that makes the equation equal on both sides.

● To solve a triangle is to find all the missing lengths and missing angles. This will normally mean using *trigonometry* and *Pythagoras*.

SPEED

This is a rate of change of distance.

The units are usually miles per hour (m.p.h.) or kilometres per hour (km/h or k.p.h.), but can also be things like metres per second (m/s) or feet per minute (ft/min).

You can find speed by finding the *gradient* on a *distance/time graph*.

Average speed

Average speed is the total distance travelled divided by the total time.

Example

Phil drove a distance of 378 miles in 8 hours. What is his average speed?

$$\text{average speed} = \frac{\text{total distance}}{\text{total time}} = \frac{378}{8} = 47.25 \text{ m.p.h}$$

✦ *distance/time graphs, gradient*

SPHERE

This is the mathematical name for a ball.
   You will not need to know any formulas about the sphere, but they do exist.

SPREAD

✦ *dispersion, inter-quartile range*

SQUARE

A square has four equal sides and four equal angles of 90°. The area of a square of side length x is x^2.
   The square has four *lines of symmetry* and has *rotational symmetry* of order 4.

Square of a number

To square a number is to multiply it by itself. For example:

- The square of 3 is 9 since $3 \times 3 = 9$.

- The square of 1.2 is 1.44 since $1.2 \times 1.2 = 1.44$.

SQUARE NUMBERS

A square number is one that has an *integer* as the square root. That is, it is a number that has come from a whole number multiplied by itself. For example,

   25 is a square number since $5 \times 5 = 25$
   289 is a square number since $17 \times 17 = 289$

The first few square numbers are 1, 4, 9, 16, 25, 36, 49, 64, 81, 100.

SQUARE ROOT

The square root of a number N is that number which, when multiplied by itself, gives you the number N. For example:

- The square root of 64 is 8 since $8 \times 8 = 64$.

- The square root of 1.21 is 1.1 since $1.1 \times 1.1 = 1.21$.

You can find the square roots of numbers on most *calculators* by the use of the key $\boxed{\sqrt{}}$. But you will usually have to round your answer off. And don't forget that each square root has two answers, the positive and the negative.

Example

What are the square roots of 30?

Type into your calculator $\boxed{30}$ $\boxed{\sqrt{}}$ to get 5.48 (rounded)
(If you have a DAL calculator then type in $\boxed{\sqrt{}}$ 30).

   The square roots of 30 then are 5.48 and –5.48.

STANDARD FORM

We use standard form to talk about very large or very small *numbers*.
   A number is expressed in standard form if it looks like the following:

   3.7×10^8

> Standard form of numbers:
> $A \times 10^n$ where $1 \leq A \leq 10$
> and n is a whole number.

For example, 3.7×10^8 is a standard form number. However, 85×10^{11} is *not* a standard form number because the 85 is not between 1 and 10. It can be changed to standard form by dividing 85 by 10, and by multiplying 10^{11} by 10, to give 8.5×10^{12}.

Putting a number into standard form

Follow the rules:

- Move the *decimal* point so that it is between the first two digits. This gives the number A.

- Count how many places you have moved the decimal point in order for it to be in that position. This gives the number n.

- If the number was a small number (less than 1) then you will need a negative sign in front of the n.

For example:

   215 000 $= 2.15 \times 10^5$
   60 000 000 $=\ \ \ 6 \times 10^7$
      0.000 000 56 $=\ \ 5.6 \times 10^{-7}$

Calculator use

All *scientific calculators* will accept numbers in standard form, and will give answers in standard form if the number is too big or too small to fit on the display.
   You put a standard form number into the calculator in a particular way. For example, to put 5×10^8 into the calculator type, in

$\boxed{5}$ $\boxed{\text{EXP}}$ $\boxed{8}$: you should see in the display $\boxed{5.\quad^{08}}$.

Calculating with standard form

Let the calculator do the work. Type each number into your calculator, making use of the memory if needed.

Example

Calculate

$$\frac{5.3 \times 10^6 \times 9.7 \times 10^9}{4.6 \times 10^{-5} \times 1.9 \times 10^{-12}}$$

● Calculate the bottom line first and put it into the memory. Enter

| 4.6 | EXP | 5 | +/– | × | 1.9 | EXP | 12 | +/– |

● Check you do this and get the display $\boxed{8.74 \quad ^{-17}}$.

● Put this into your memory and enter the top line to get a display of $\boxed{5.141 \quad ^{16}}$.

● Now just divide your display by the memory recall to get the display $\boxed{5.882151 \quad ^{32}}$, which we round off and write as 5.9×10^{32}.

Example KS3 question

(a) A space ship travelled from Earth to Mars. It travelled 3.5×10^7 miles. The journey took approximately 7000 hours. What was the speed of the space ship?

(b) Another space ship travelled from Earth to Jupiter. It travelled 3.9×10^8 miles, taking about 12 000 hours. How many times as fast is the second space ship?

Solution

Use your calculator and do as much as you can in standard form.

(a) Speed = distance ÷ time = $3.5 \times 10^7 \div 7000$ = 5000 m.p.h.

(b) Speed = $3.9 \times 10^8 \div 12\,000$ = 32 500 m.p.h.
So the second ship is 32 500 ÷ 5000 = 6.5 times faster than the first.

↔ *power*

STATISTICS

Statistics are pieces of information.
    We use statistics to inform us of what is happening, what might happen, and why it might be happening. Statistics is an important part of mathematics, and perhaps a part that you will use in life almost as much as arithmetic.
    Statistics is such a wide topic that you will find it distributed all over this book. It covers the following.

Display

There are many ways of displaying the information gathered to show the relative frequencies: *bar charts*, *pictograms*, *pie charts*, *histograms*, *frequency* polygons, *scatter graphs*.

Averages

Once we have some data we usually want to know the *average*, but there are three different types of average you can use: *mode*, *median*, *mean*.

Frequency

How many pieces of data do we have? The number is called the *frequency*, but this frequency can be used in different ways: frequency tables, *grouped* frequency, *cumulative frequency*.

Distribution

We often want to compare one set of data with another. This is done by looking at the distribution in one of the following different ways: *range*, *inter-quartile range*.

SUBJECT

This is the term or letter on its own, usually to the left of the = sign. For example, in $y = 3x$, y is the subject of the expression.

SUBSTITUTION

This is where you replace a letter in an expression or formula with a number. For example, if

$$y = 3t + 4$$

and I substitute 5 for t, then

$$y = 3 \times 5 + 4 = 19$$

There are many times when you will be substituting values into expressions and formulas, and it is something you need to be able to do well.

Example KS3 question

Use the formula

$$t = \frac{m^2 - p^2}{3g}$$

to find t when $g = -7.5$, $m = 3$, $p = 13$. Show your working.

Solution

You need to show what and how you have substituted.

$$t = \frac{3^2 - 13^2}{3 \times -7.5} = \frac{9 - 169}{-22.5} = \frac{-160}{-22.5} = 7.111\ 111\ 1$$

= 7.1 (rounded)

algebra

SUBTENDS

A word sometimes used to refer to the angle an *arc* makes at the centre of a circle.

SUM

The sum of two numbers is the result of adding them together. For example, the sum of 3 and 5 is 8 since 3 + 5 = 8.

SUPPLEMENTARY ANGLES

Two angles are supplementary if they add up to 180°.
    Supplementary angles occur in the following situations.

Angles on a line

The two angles in Figure S.21 will always add up to 180°.

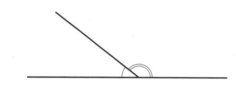

Figure S.21 Angles on a line

Parallels

The two angles inside the parallel in Figure S.22 will add up to 180°.

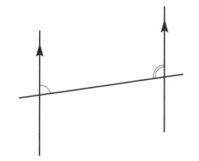

Figure S.22 Angles inside a parallel line

SYMMETRY

Plane shapes can have symmetry, and *solid shapes* can have symmetry.

Plane shapes

There are two types of symmetry: line and rotational.

Line symmetry

If you can fold a shape over so that one half fits exactly on top of the other half, then the line over which you folded is a *line of symmetry*.
    Figure S.23 presents some shapes with their lines of symmetry shown by dashed lines.

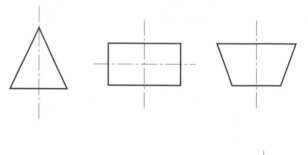

Figure S.23

Rotational symmetry

A shape has rotational symmetry if it can be turned around the centre of the shape and occupy exactly the same space in at least one other position.
    The order of rotational symmetry of a shape is the number of different positions that the shape can occupy in the same space while turning around the centre of the shape.
    Figure S.24 presents some shapes with their order of rotational symmetry given.

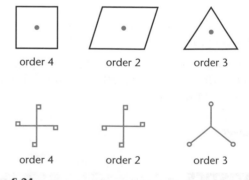

Figure S.24

Warning: every shape has an order of rotational symmetry. If a shape has no rotational symmetry then its order is 1, since there is only one position in which it can occupy the same space.

For example the shape in Figure S.25 has *no* rotational symmetry but it has rotational symmetry of order 1.

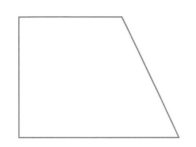

Figure S.25

Solid shapes

There are two types of symmetry, planes of symmetry and axes of symmetry.

Planes of symmetry

A shape has a plane of symmetry if you can slice the shape into two matching halves, one the exact mirror image of the other.

For example, Figure S.26 shows a cuboid which has been sliced in three different ways to give the same shape on both sides. The plane of symmetry is where we have sliced it.

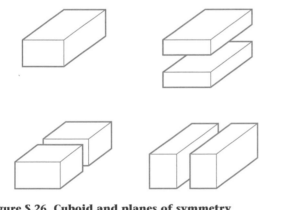

Figure S.26 Cuboid and planes of symmetry

Axes of symmetry

An axis of symmetry is a line through which a shape can turn so that it occupies the same space. Its order is how many such turns there are.

For example, Figure S.27 shows a square based pyramid. It has an axis of symmetry of order 4.

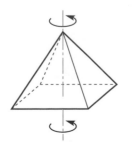

Figure S.27 Square based pyramid and axis of symmetry

Example KS3 question

(a) Draw in, on the shapes in Figure S.28, all the lines of symmetry. If a shape has no lines of symmetry then say so.

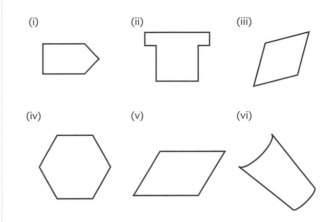

Figure S.28

(b) State the order of rotational symmetry for each shape.

Solution

(a) You should have no lines of symmetry for shape (v). I hope you noticed that two of the shapes have more than one line of symmetry. The shapes (other than (v)) should have lines of symmetry as in Figure S.29.

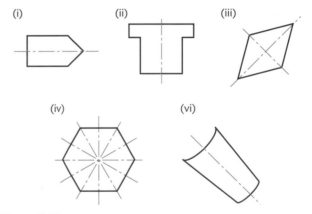

Figure S.29

(b) The orders of rotational symmetry are:

(i) 1   (ii) 1   (iii) 2   (iv) 6   (v) 2   (vi) 1

TALLY

You tally when making a tally chart. A tally chart is what you use on a data capture form.

Example

Make a data capture form to see which is the favourite lesson out of maths, English, science, humanities, technology or sport and leisure.

Lesson	Tally	Frequency
Maths	1̶1̶1̶1̶ 1̶1̶1̶1̶ 1̶1̶1̶1̶ 11	17
English	1̶1̶1̶1̶ 111	8
Science	1̶1̶1̶1̶ 1̶1̶1̶1̶ 111	13
Humanities	1̶1̶1̶1̶ 1̶1̶1̶1̶	10
Technology	1̶1̶1̶1̶ 1̶1̶1̶1̶ 11	12
Sport and leisure	1̶1̶1̶1̶ 11	7
Total		67

The tallies are **gated**: that is, there is a line through each four to make a five. This helps when counting the tallies to complete the frequency column.

◈ *data collection sheet, frequency*

TANGENT

There are two types of tangents used in mathematics.

Trigonometry tangent (tan)

The tangent (abbreviated tan) in trigonometry is a ratio used to solve problems in *right angled triangles*. The definition of tangent θ is

$$\tan \theta = \frac{\text{opposite}}{\text{adjacent}}$$

See Figure T.1.

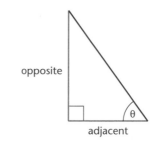

Figure T.1

Example 1

Find the length x in Figure T.2.

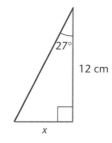

Figure T.2

From the triangle we can say that:

$$\tan 27° = \frac{\text{opposite}}{\text{adjacent}} = \frac{x}{12}$$

Then

$$12 \tan 27° = x$$

(12 tan 27° means 12 multiplied by tan 27°.) This is done on a *scientific calculator* by one of two methods, depending on the type of calculator:

DAL: type as it reads [12] [tan] [27] [=]

Others: type in as [12] [×] [27] [tan] [=]

(notice you need the 27 before the tan)

Check you can do this on *your* calculator to get $x = 6.11$ cm (rounded).

Example 2

Find the angle θ in Figure T.3.

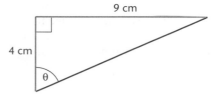

Figure T.3

From the triangle we can say that:

$$\tan \theta = \frac{\text{opposite}}{\text{adjacent}} = \frac{9}{4}$$

$$\tan \theta = \frac{9}{4} = 2.25$$

We use this fact to find the size of angle θ. With 2.25 in the calculator, type into the calculator $\boxed{\tan^{-1}}$ which is usually found by

$\boxed{\text{shift}}$ $\boxed{\text{tan}}$ or $\boxed{\text{inv}}$ $\boxed{\text{tan}}$ or $\boxed{\text{2ndf}}$ $\boxed{\text{tan}}$

Check that you can do this on *your* calculator to get θ = 66° (rounded).

Tangent to a circle

The other tangent is the line that just touches a circle at one point (Figure T.4). A tangent to a circle is always *perpendicular* to the radius of the circle.

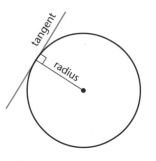

Figure T.4

TERMINATING

A terminating *decimal* is one that has a fixed number of decimal places. For example,

$1/2 = 0.5$ $1/4 = 0.25$ $3/5 = 0.6$ $7/8 = 0.875$

In fact, any fraction with a bottom number of 2, 4, 5, 8 or 10 will always be a terminating decimal.

If a decimal is not terminal then it is most likely to be a *recurring* decimal.

TESSELLATION

Regular tessellations

A regular tessellation is a regular pattern made from one basic shape that will cover a large flat surface without leaving any gaps (apart from at the very edges). Some examples are shown in Figure T.5.

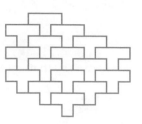

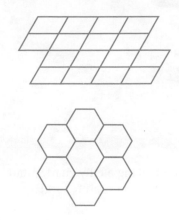

Figure T.5

Note that:

- Every *triangle* will tessellate.
- Every *quadrilateral* will tessellate.
- Regular *hexagons* will tessellate.

Semi-regular tessellations

A semi-regular tessellation is one which uses two shapes only to completely fill a large flat area (except perhaps for the edges). An example is shown in Figure T.6.

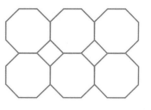

Figure T.6

TETRAHEDRON

A tetrahedron is a *solid shape* made up of four faces, each one a triangle.

A regular tetrahedron has each face an equilateral triangle (Figure T.7).

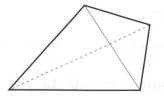

Figure T.7

TIME

✛ *distance/time graphs, travel graphs, unit*

TONNE

The tonne is also known as the *metric* ton.

1 tonne = 1000 kilograms
1 tonne = 0.9842 tons

An approximation for the weight of 1 tonne is the weight of a farm horse.

TRANSFORMATION

A transformation is a change.

In mathematics a transformation will refer to one of the following changes to a shape: *reflection*, *rotation*, *enlargement* and *translation*.

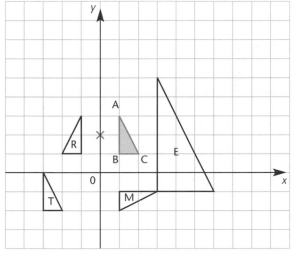

Figure T.8

Examples

Figure T.8 shows each type of transformation on the shaded triangle ABC:

- R is the result of a reflection in the *y*-axis.

- M is the result of a rotation of 90° clockwise about the origin.

- E is the result of an enlargement of scale factor 3 from the point (0, 2).

- T is the result of a translation of

$$\begin{pmatrix} -4 \\ -3 \end{pmatrix}$$

enlargement, reflection, rotation, translation

TRANSLATION

A translation is a type of *transformation*.

It is a movement, sometimes called a slide, using horizontal and vertical displacement. This displacement is put together in what is called a *vector*. The displacement moves *every* point in the shape in exactly the same way.

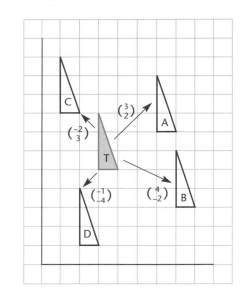

Figure T.9

Example

Figure T.9 shows how the triangle T has been translated with different vectors:

- T has been translated to A with the vector $\begin{pmatrix} 3 \\ 2 \end{pmatrix}$: three right, two up.

- T has been translated to B with the vector $\begin{pmatrix} 4 \\ -2 \end{pmatrix}$: four right, two down.

- T has been translated to C with the vector $\begin{pmatrix} -2 \\ 3 \end{pmatrix}$: two left, three up.

- T has been translated to D with the vector $\begin{pmatrix} -1 \\ -4 \end{pmatrix}$: one left, four down.

Notice how the negative is used to indicate movement to the left and down.

transformation, vector

TRANSPOSITION

Transposition is the mathematical word for 'change a formula around'. We often need to transpose when we change the *subject* of a *formula*.

When you transpose a formula you use the same rules as when you manipulate equations. That is, you move things from one side of an equation to the other; when it has changed, it must do the opposite thing.

> Remember: you can only move something from one side to the other if it's doing what it's doing to everything else on that side.

Follow through these examples to see how we transpose formulas.

Example 1

$t = 4m - 1$: make m the subject.

We first move the –1 to give

$$t + 1 = 4m$$

Now we move the 4 to give

$$\frac{t + 1}{4} = m$$

Hence

$$m = \frac{t + 1}{4}$$

Example 2

$k = \dfrac{5h + 4}{m}$: make h the subject.

We first move the m to give

$$mk = 5h + 4$$

Now we move the +4 to give

$$mk - 4 = 5h$$

Now move the 5 to give

$$\frac{mk - 4}{5} = h$$

Hence

$$h = \frac{mk - 4}{5}$$

Example 3

$W = t + m^2$: make m the subject.

We first move the t to give

$$W - t = m^2$$

Now we move the square to give

$$\sqrt{(W - t)} = m$$

Hence

$$m = \sqrt{(W - t)}$$

TRANSVERSAL

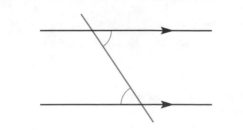

Figure T.10

A transversal is a straight line passing through two or more parallel lines. A transversal creates alternate angles that are equal to each other: see Figure T.10.

TRAPEZIUM

A trapezium is a *quadrilateral* that has just two parallel sides (Figure T.11).

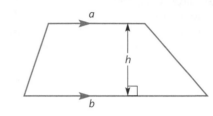

Figure T.11

The area of a trapezium is given by

$$\text{area} = \frac{h}{2}\,(a + b)$$

where a and b are the lengths of the parallel sides and h is the perpendicular distance between them.

Example

Find the area of the shape in Figure T.12.

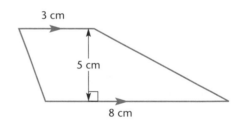

Figure T.12

Use the formula to give

$$\text{area} = \frac{5}{2}\,(3 + 8) = 27.5 \text{ cm}^2$$

✦ *isosceles*

TRAVEL GRAPH

These are *graphs* which show how the distance or the speed has varied with time. They are most common with straight lines from point to point, but can be drawn with curves.

There are two types of travel graphs: distance/time and velocity/time.

Distance/time graph

Look at the example of a *distance/time graph* in Figure T.13. It represents a coach leaving Sheffield to travel towards Scotland.

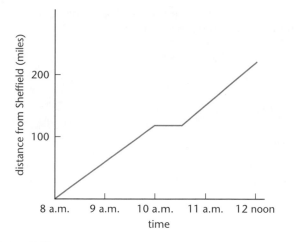

Figure T.13

- It shows that the coach left at 8.00 a.m.

- It shows that in the first two hours the coach travelled a distance of 120 miles. This represents a speed of 60 m.p.h.

- The bus stopped from 10.00 a.m. to 10.30 a.m. and then covered the next 100 miles in 1½ hours.

The *gradient* of the lines represents the speed. The gradient of the line representing the second stage of the journey is given by

$$100 \div 1.5 = 66.7 \text{ (rounded)}$$

Hence this speed is 66.7 m.p.h.

Velocity/time graph

Velocity is speed in a given direction.

Look at the example of a velocity/time graph in Figure T.14. It represents the velocity of a cross-country runner. It shows the run starting at 10.00 a.m. and the runner starting very quickly, then settling down to a steady coasting speed of 8 m.p.h. At 11.15 a.m. he must have seen the finishing line because he picks up speed and accelerates to a top speed. He crosses the line with a flourish, and very quickly slows down to stop.

The gradient of a line in a velocity/time graph will give acceleration.

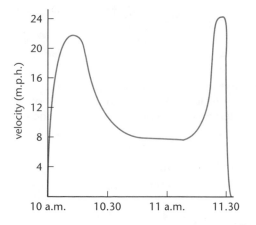

Figure T.14

TREE DIAGRAM

A tree diagram is used in *probability* to illustrate all the possibilities and to help see the whole situation with all associated probabilities.

Example

In a bag were 10 beads, 8 blue and 2 white. Two are taken out at random. What are the probabilities of taking out (a) two of the same colour, (b) at least one white?

A tree diagram can be drawn as in Figure T.15.

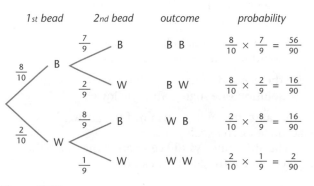

Figure T.15

The probabilities of the single events have been put on the branches. Notice that for the 'second bead' the probabilities have to assume that the first bead has been taken out, which is why those probabilities are different.

The probabilities of the combined events have been *multiplied* using the **AND** rule.

(a) This can be answered using the *OR rule*, since we want the probability of taking out two blue **OR** two white. The **OR** rule says we need to *ADD* the probabilities:

$$\frac{56}{90} + \frac{2}{90} = \frac{58}{90}$$

You would cancel this down to 29/45.

(b) The probability of at least one white is
1 – probability of *no* white, or
1 – probability of two blue. This is

$$1 - \frac{56}{90} = \frac{34}{90}$$

You would cancel this down to 17/45.

Tree diagrams are not essential to solve probability problems, but they can help us to see the whole situation at once.

✥ *probability*

TREND

The pattern between variables.

✥ *correlation*

TRIAL AND IMPROVEMENT

This is the technique used to solve a problem which cannot be solved by conventional means.
For example,

● Find a value of x for which $x^2 + x = 60$.

Yes, this can be solved by higher mathematics, but most of you can only solve it by trial and improvement.
The technique implies that you make a trial (an intelligent guess), and then keep improving that trial with more trials based on previous trials. You find:

1 the two whole numbers closest to a solution, one higher and one lower

2 the two 1 decimal place numbers closest to the solution, one higher and one lower.

3 the two 2 decimal place numbers closest to the solution one higher and one lower.

You can carry on like this until the answer is as accurate as you wish.
The aim is always to keep narrowing down the places where the solution can be.

Example
Follow through the solution to $x^2 + x = 60$.

Trial: x	Working: $x^2 + x$	High/low	Comment
7	$7^2 + 7 = 56$	low	try higher
8	$8^2 + 8 = 72$	high	it's between 7 and 8, go for 7.5
7.5	$7.5^2 + 7.5 = 63.75$	high	between 7 and 7.5, go for 7.3
7.3	$7.3^2 + 7.3 = 60.59$	high	only just, try 7.2
7.2	$7.2^2 + 7.2 = 59.04$	low	between 7.2 and 7.3, go for 7.25
7.25	$= 59.8125$	low	between 7.25 and 7.30, go for 7.27
7.27	$= 60.1229$	high	between 7.25 and 7.27, go for 7.26
7.26	$= 59.9676$	low	between 7.26 and 7.27

Clearly we could carry on like this for a long time, getting closer and closer. We can stop around here if we want the answer to two decimal places. All we have to do is to decide which is the closer answer, 7.26 or 7.27?
We do *not* choose the one that gives the closest answer to 60. That technique does not always produce the closest solution, since the equation is quadratic. We decide which is the closest solution by looking half-way between 7.26 and 7.27, which is 7.265. This gives the answer 60.045 225, which is too high. This gives us the situation:

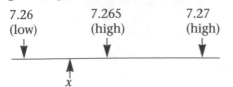

7.26   7.265   7.27
(low)   (high)   (high)

x

The x must be between the 7.26 and the 7.265: hence 7.26 is the 2 decimal solution.

> *Care has to be taken to make sure you apply the trial and improvement technique correctly. It is not a trial and error method with lots of wild guesses.*

Notice how we got as close as we could with whole numbers, then 1 decimal place numbers, then 2 decimal place numbers, finally using the 3 decimal place number to find the closest 2 decimal place solution.

Example KS3 question 1
The equation $x^2 + x = 15$ has two solutions. Andrew finds that 3 and 4 are the closest whole numbers to one of the solutions.

x	$x^2 + x$
3	12
4	20

Find the 2 decimal place solution in this range.

Solution
You first need to find the 1 decimal place pair closest to the solution:

x	$x^2 + x$	
3.5	15.75	high
3.3	14.19	low
3.4	14.96	low

So we know the solution is between 3.4 and 3.5.
We now go for the pair of 2 decimal place numbers closest to the solution:

x	$x^2 + x$	
3.45	15.3525	high
3.42	15.1164	high
3.41	15.0381	high

So we know the solution is between 3.40 and 3.41.
To find the closest solution we have to look at 3.405, which gives 14.999 025 (small). So the closest must be 3.41.

Example KS3 question 2
Mark and Gary are using the expression

$$\frac{n}{2}(n+1)$$

to generate triangle numbers. For example, the triangle number for $n = 3$ is

$$\frac{3}{2}(3 + 1)$$

which gives the number 6.

(a) Mark wants to find the largest triangle number less than 500. Use trial and improvement to find this number.

(b) Gary wants to find the smallest triangle number bigger than 1000. What is this number?

Solution

(a) You need to make a series of trials, and show an improvement in getting closer.

n	$\frac{n}{2}(n + 1)$	
20	210	low
40	820	high
30	465	low
35	630	high
32	528	high
31	496	low

So the largest number less than 500 which is a triangle number is 31. (Notice how I found the nearest 10 first, then improved the trial.)

(b) You now set about the number over 1000 in a similar way.

n	$\frac{n}{2}(n + 1)$	
40	820	low
50	1275	high
45	1035	high
44	990	low

So we quickly find the smallest triangle number larger than 1000: it is 1035.

✦ *equations*

TRIANGLE

A triangle is a three sided *polygon*. The angles inside a triangle always add up to 180°.

The area of a triangle is given by the formula (Figure T.16):

$$\text{area of a triangle} = \frac{\text{base} \times \text{height}}{2}$$

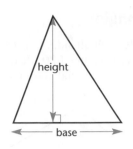

Figure T.16

Isosceles triangle

An isosceles triangle (Figure T.17) has two sides the same length, and the angles at the bottom of the equal sides are also equal. It has one line of symmetry straight down the middle. It has no rotational symmetry.

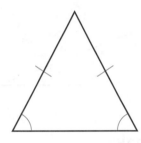

Figure T.17

Equilateral triangle

An equilateral triangle (Figure T.18) has all its sides the same length and all its angles equal to 60°. It has three lines of symmetry as shown. It has rotational symmetry of order 3.

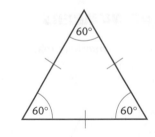

Figure T.18

Right angled triangle

This is a triangle that has a right angle in it (Figure T.19). The longest side, opposite the 90°, is called the *hypotenuse*.

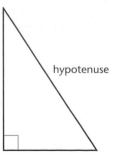

Figure T.19

Scalene triangle

This is a triangle with all sides a different length, and all angles different (Figure T.20). It has no lines of symmetry and no rotational symmetry.

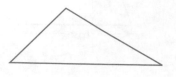

Figure T.20

Obtuse angles triangle

This is a triangle that contains an obtuse angle (Figure T.21). It could also be isosceles, but it cannot be right angled.

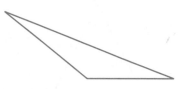

Figure T.21

Solving triangles

When asked to solve a triangle, you must find all the lengths and all the angles. This is usually done with the help of *trigonometry* and *Pythagoras*.

✦ *congruent, similar, trigonometry,*
  line of symmetry, rotational symmetry

TRIANGULAR NUMBERS

This is the sequence of *numbers* made by considering how many balls can be put together to create an *equilateral* triangle around them (Figure T.22).

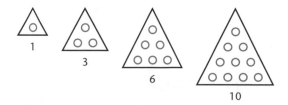

Figure T.22

See how the sequence builds up by adding onto each successive term one more than was added previously. This gives the sequence of triangle numbers as:

1, 3, 6, 10, 15, 21, 28, 36, 45, 55, 66, 78 ...

The *n*th triangular number is given by

$$\frac{n\,(n+1)}{2}$$

TRIGONOMETRY

This is the study of angles and sides in triangles.

We only deal here with right angle trigonometry (other triangles are higher maths). This falls into the three parts of *sine*, *cosine* and *tangent*.

It is based on *right angled triangles* where each side is defined as follows (Figure T.23):

● The longest side opposite the 90° is called the *hypotenuse*.

● The side opposite the identified angle is called the *opposite*.

● The side next to both the 90° and the identified angle is called the *adjacent*.

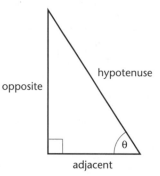

Figure T.23

The relationships are all built around these sides as defined:

$$\text{sine } \theta = \frac{\text{opposite}}{\text{hypotenuse}}$$

$$\text{cosine } \theta = \frac{\text{adjacent}}{\text{hypotenuse}}$$

$$\text{tangent } \theta = \frac{\text{opposite}}{\text{adjacent}}$$

This is best learnt by some saying or mnemonic such as:

Silly Old Hitler Couldn't Advance His Troops Over Africa

The first letters of these words give

$$S = \frac{O}{H} \quad C = \frac{A}{H} \quad T = \frac{O}{A}$$

which remind us of the three relationships.

Shorthand

You will find that the full trigonometrical names are not used. They are shortened as follows:

- sine: sin
- cosine: cos
- tangent: tan

and it is these keys that you will find on your calculators.

Solving problems

If you have a problem to solve that involves trigonometry, then:

1 Draw a triangle.

2 Put on the given information.

3 Decide which bit of trigonometry you need.

Example 1

A 3 metre ladder is leaning against a wall, making an angle of 70° with the floor. Calculate how high up the wall the ladder reaches.

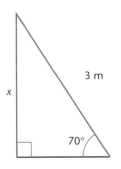

Figure T.24

First draw a diagram and put on the given information (Figure T.24). Now you can see that the only sides in the question that we need to bother about are opposite and hypotenuse. This links us to 'Silly Old Hitler', which is the reminder for

$$\sin \theta = \frac{\text{opposite}}{\text{hypotenuse}}$$

Substitute the given values into this equation to give us

$$\sin 70° = \frac{x}{3}$$

Hence

$$3 \sin 70° = x$$

(3 sin 70° means 3 multiplied by sin 70°.) This is calculated in one of two ways depending on the type of *calculator* you have:

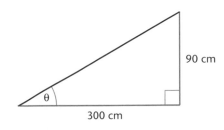

DAL: type as it reads [3] [sin] [70] [=]
Others: type in as [3] [×] [70] [sin] [=]
  (notice you need the 70 before the sin)

Check you can do this on *your* calculator to get the x = 2.8 m (rounded).

Example 2

A bird is sitting on a bird table 90 cm high. It sees a worm on the ground 300 cm away from the foot of the bird table. It flies straight to the worm. What angle to the ground does the bird fly at?

Figure T.25

First draw a triangle and put on the given information (Figure T.25). We see that the given sides are opposite and adjacent. This links us to 'Troops Over Africa', which is the reminder for

$$\tan \theta = \frac{\text{opposite}}{\text{adjacent}}$$

Substitute the given values into this equation to give us

$$\tan \theta = \frac{90}{300} = 0.3$$

We use this fact to find the size of angle θ. With 0.3 in the calculator, type in tan⁻¹ which is usually found by

[shift] [tan] or [inv] [tan] or [2ndf] [tan]

Check that you can do this on *your* calculator to get θ° = 16.7° (rounded).

TRILLION

A trillion is a million million, that is 10^{12} or 1 000 000 000 000.

TRUNCATE

You truncate a decimal number by just chopping off so many decimal places. For example, if instead of 5.7839 you write down 5.7, you have truncated instead of rounding off.

Some basic calculators do this with decimal numbers that do not fit into their display, and you need to be careful if you're using such a calculator.

> You should not *truncate any decimal.*
> You should always be **rounding** off.

UNIT

A unit is a single thing.

Units are what we use to define *length*, weight, time, *capacity*, *area* and *volume*. We are concerned with the *metric* and *imperial* systems of units.

Length units

Imperial

Units: inch (in), feet (ft), yard (yd), mile (mi).

```
  12 inches  = 1 foot
   3 feet    = 1 yard
1760 yards   = 1 mile
```

Metric

Units: millimetres (mm), centimetres (cm), metres (m), kilometres (km).

```
  10 millimetres  = 1 centimetre
 100 centimetres  = 1 metre
1000 metres       = 1 kilometre
```

Conversions

```
1 inch ≈ 2.54 centimetres
1 mile ≈   1.6 kilometres
```

Weight units

Imperial

Units: ounces (oz), pounds (lb), stones, hundredweight (cwt), tons.

```
16 ounces         = 1 pound
14 pounds         = 1 stone
 8 stones         = 1 hundredweight
20 hundredweight  = 1 ton
```

Metric

Units: grams (g), kilograms (kg) and tonnes (t).

```
1000 grams      = 1 kilogram
1000 kilograms  = 1 tonne
```

Conversions

```
1 ounce    ≈ 28.35 grams
2.2 pounds ≈ 1 kilogram
1 ton      ≈ 1.0161 tonnes
```

Capacity units

Imperial

Units: pints (pt) and gallons (gal).

```
8 pints = 1 gallon
```

Metric

Units: millilitres (ml), centilitres (cl) and litres (l).

```
1000 millilitres = 1 litre
 100 centilitres = 1 litre
```

Conversions

1 gallon ≈ 4.5461 litres

Time units

Units: second (s), minute (min), hour (h), day (d), etc.

Area units

Units are length units squared, e.g. m^2, km^2, cm^2, etc.

Volume units

Units are length units cubed, e.g. m^3, cm^3, km^3, etc.

Example KS3 question

Each measurement below can be given in different units. Give the correct unit to make the sentence sensible.

(a) The height of the boy is (i) 147 ... or (ii) 5 ....

(b) The weight of the 6 year old boy is 32 ....

(c) The amount of milk in a cupful is 100 ....

Solution

(a) (i) Has to be centimetres (cm).
    (ii) Has to be feet (ft).

(b) Has to be kilograms (kg).

(c) Has to be cubic centimetres (cm^3) or millilitres (ml).

UPPER QUARTILE

That value above which 25% of the total distribution lies.

✦ *cumulative frequency, quartiles*

V

VANISHING POINT

⟡ *perspective*

VARIABLE

A variable is something that changes.
   In mathematics a variable is usually a letter in **algebra**. For example,

   area of a triangle = $\frac{1}{2}bh$

where b and h are variables.

VARIATION

This is another word for **proportion**.

VECTOR

A vector is what we use to describe a **translation**.
   It is shown as two numbers put in a column, e.g.

$$\begin{pmatrix} 2 \\ 3 \end{pmatrix}$$

The top number refers to the horizontal movement of the translation. The bottom number refers to the vertical movement.
   Negative numbers in a vector represent movement to the left or down.

Example

Some vectors are shown in Figure V.1:

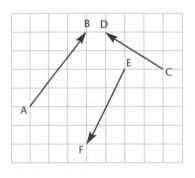

Figure V.1

   AB   represents the vector $\begin{pmatrix} 3 \\ 4 \end{pmatrix}$

   CD   represents the vector $\begin{pmatrix} -3 \\ 2 \end{pmatrix}$

   EF   represents the vector $\begin{pmatrix} -2 \\ -4 \end{pmatrix}$

> *There is a lot more to vectors than this, but wait until higher maths to see it!*

VELOCITY

This is **speed** with a direction.

⟡ *graphs, travel graphs*

VERTEX

A vertex is a point where two (or more) lines or edges meet. The plural of 'vertex' is 'vertices'.
   The vertices of a triangle are the sharp corners where the lines meet (Figure V.2).

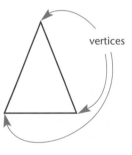

vertices

Figure V.2

The vertex of a pyramid is the top point. However, note that there are also vertices at the corners of the square base (Figure V.3).

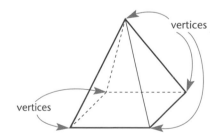

vertices

vertices

Figure V.3

VERTICAL

A line is vertical if it is at right angles to the horizontal (ground) (Figure V.4).

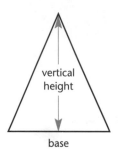

Figure V.4

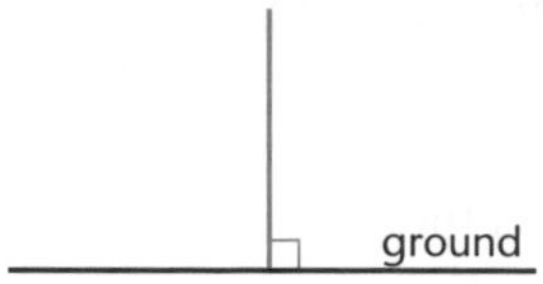

A vertical height is at right angles to the base (Figure V.5). For example,

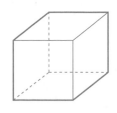

Figure V.5

area of a triangle = $\frac{1}{2}$ × base × vertical height

VERTICALLY OPPOSITE ANGLES

Two pairs of equal angles formed by the *intersection* of two straight lines.

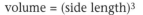 *intersection*

VOLUME

The volume is the amount of three dimensional space a *solid shape* occupies.
    Volume formula you will meet are the following.

Cube

In Figure V.6,

volume = (side length)³

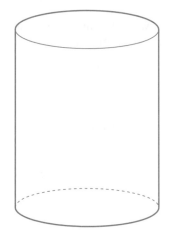

Figure V.6

Cuboid

In Figure V.7,

volume = length × width × height

128

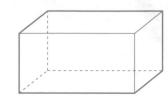

Figure V.7

Prism

In Figure V.8,

volume = area of regular cross-section × length

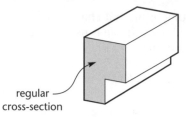

regular cross-section

Figure V.8

Cylinder

In Figure V.9,

volume = π × (radius)² × height

Figure V.9

VULGAR FRACTION

A vulgar fraction is one made up of a top number and a bottom number, such as $\frac{3}{4}$.

Equivalent vulgar fractions

Any vulgar fraction has an infinity of fractions equivalent to it.
    Vulgar fractions can be cancelled down to create equivalent fractions. You cancel down by dividing both top and bottom by the same number. For example,

$$\frac{6}{8} = \frac{3}{4} \quad \text{(6 and 8 both divided by 2)}$$

To add or subtract two vulgar fractions

You can only add or subtract two vulgar fractions that have the same bottom number. So the first thing to do is to make sure that you change one or both of the fractions to create equivalent fractions with the same bottom number. Then it's a simple job of adding or subtracting the tops.

Example 1

$$\frac{2}{5} + \frac{1}{3}$$

First create equivalent fractions. We ask ourselves 'What can I make both 5 and 3 into by multiplying?' This is easy!! It's 3×5, which is 15. So make both bottom numbers 15 by multiplying:

$$\frac{2 \times 3}{5 \times 3} = \frac{6}{15} \text{ and } \frac{1}{3} \times \frac{5}{5} = \frac{5}{15}$$

Hence

$$\frac{2}{5} + \frac{1}{3} = \frac{6}{15} + \frac{5}{15} = \frac{11}{15}$$

Example 2

$$\frac{7}{8} - \frac{5}{6}$$

Again we need to find what we can change both bottoms into. Looking at 8 and 6, the smallest number they can both be made into is 24. (We could again have used $6 \times 8 = 48$, but the smaller the number the better.) So make both bottom numbers 24 by multiplying:

$$\frac{7 \times 3}{8 \times 3} = \frac{21}{24} \text{ and } \frac{5 \times 4}{6 \times 4} = \frac{20}{24}$$

Hence

$$\frac{7}{8} - \frac{5}{6} = \frac{21}{24} - \frac{20}{24} = \frac{1}{24}$$

To multiply two vulgar fractions

This is easy, since all we do is

- multiply the tops
- multiply the bottoms
- cancel if necessary.

You can cancel beforehand if you wish; any top can cancel with any bottom.

Example 3

$$\frac{3}{4} \times \frac{5}{8}$$

This is done by simply multiplying tops and bottoms:

$$\frac{3}{4} \times \frac{5}{8} = \frac{15}{32} \text{ (nothing will cancel)}$$

Example 4

$$\frac{5}{12} \times \frac{8}{9}$$

This can be done by multiplying tops and bottoms:

$$\frac{5}{12} \times \frac{8}{9} = \frac{40}{108} = \frac{10}{27} \text{ (cancelling top and bottom by 4)}$$

Note that you could have cancelled at the beginning of the calculation by dividing the top 8 and the bottom 12 both by 4. This would have left you with:

$$\frac{5}{3} \times \frac{2}{9} = \frac{10}{27}$$

This is a much simpler sum since the numbers are smaller.

✦ *fractions*

WEIGHT

✦ *imperial, metric, mass, unit*

WHOLE NUMBERS

These are the numbers 1, 2, 3, 4, 5, 6, 7, 8 .... There can be negative whole numbers also, namely –1, –2, –3, –4 ....

The mathematical name for whole numbers is *integers*.